What readers say ‹
Parkinson's Dream

MW00620164

"Rick Hermann entered into this writing to explore the mystery and clarity of living with Parkinson's disease. He writes with seriousness and humor of a life that not only continues to evolve but finds connections between PD and music, modern dance, literature, movies, horses, parking spots, gratitude, brain surgery, sadness, and silliness. Living with Parkinson's has helped him explore the truth of who he might really be. As layers of ability and certainty are progressively peeled away, he finds clues that bring him closer to an answer to the existential question, 'Who am I?'"

— Richard Scholtz, Co-director, Health Neighborhood
Mapping project for the Critical Junctures Institute;
music educator; community healthcare advocate

"This is deceptively straightforward stuff, but you eventually find yourself treading deep waters."

— Kathleen Karella, MSW, LCSW, and PD patient

This is unlike any other book on Parkinson's disease out there ... distinctive story-telling and [a] fresh, engaging manner. Rick's words also invite the reader to contemplate universal themes: the need for validation, the power and essential nature of living in the present, feeling deep loss, maintaining hope, struggling with identity.

— Barbara Mathers-Schmidt, Chair,
Department of Communication Sciences and Disorders,
Western Washington University

About the Author

Rick Hermann has written for *Movietone News, Northwest Book Arts* magazine, *Washington* magazine, and the *Seattle Weekly*. In 2011, he published his first collection of short stories, *The Bright World of Dandelion Court*. He lives in Bellingham, Washington, with his wife Lee Willis and their bed-hogging tuxedo cat Abby.

Parkinson's Dreams about Me

My Dance with the Shaking Palsy

Also by Rick Hermann

The Bright World of Dandelion Court:
stories and other lies (2011)

Praise for
The Bright World of Dandelion Court

"Rick Hermann, who has been living with Parkinson's disease for the past 20 years, knows a thing or two about disequilibrium. Bold in subject matter, sly in delivery, Hermann, in *The Bright World of Dandelion Court*, writes about the 'mental fibrillations' that animate and bedevil his characters. It's fascinating stuff, no less frightening for the normalcy that many of the characters project.... The careful crafting of these narratives makes for a worthwhile read."

— Barbara Lloyd McMichael, *Tacoma News Tribune*

Parkinson's Dreams about Me

My Dance with the Shaking Palsy

Rick Hermann

Foreword by
Barbara Mathers-Schmidt, Ph.D.

Parkinson's Dreams about Me:
My Dance with the Shaking Palsy
Rick Hermann
Foreword by Barbara Mathers-Schmidt, Ph.D.

Copyeditors: Elizabeth Weber, Lee Willis
Proofreader: Libby Lewis
Book design and prepress: Kate Weisel, weiselcreative.com

ISBN 978-0-9858074-0-5 (pbk)
ISBN 978-0-9858074-1-2 (ebook)

Order at: http://rickhermann.wordpress.com/

To order Rick Hermann's previous book, *The Bright World of Dandelion Court: stories and other lies,* contact Village Books, 1200 11th Street, Bellingham, WA 98225, or on the Web at www.villagebooks.com.

Manufactured in the United States of America

For Lee and Eli,
who inspired me to complete this book.

Involuntary tremulous motion … with a propensity to bend the trunk forwards, and to pass from a walking to a running pace: the senses and intellects being uninjured.

— James Parkinson, "An Essay on the Shaking Palsy," published in 1817

Contents

PART ONE
My Parkinson's Disease Chronology

PART TWO
Living with Parkinson's Disease

PART THREE

Foreword

In 2011 one of my graduate students and I embarked on a study to better understand the needs, concerns, and desires of local people who are living with idiopathic Parkinson's disease (PD). We had determined that "community based participatory research" (CBPR) would be the optimal approach. In CBPR community members affected by a problem are actively engaged in all aspects of the study—from developing the research questions to identifying action based on findings. They are equal partners with the academicians. As a first step we needed to recruit the participant partners. Fortunately our quest led us to a university dance instructor who suggested Rick Hermann, who was diagnosed with PD in 1998. Through our combined efforts we have become a group of 11 members—nine people who have been diagnosed with idiopathic PD and two speech-language pathologists with clinical, research, and personal interests in PD.

It is fairly well known that people with PD likely will experience communication problems at some point. During my 35 years working as a speech-language pathologist I have witnessed the multiple ways in which communication can become impaired as PD impacts speech and voice and even cognition. Ultimately this can have a huge impact on communication participation and quality of life. I also have been frustrated to see how many clients who seek our services are self-referred. Hence my intention was to concentrate on the communication-related concerns and needs of our participants, and I assumed this would be a shared concern of the members in our first focus group meeting.

Not so. After a few false starts and puzzled efforts of community members to respond to the graduate student's prompts, it was clear something needed to change. With a nudge from Rick the conversation shifted to members sharing deeply and personally relevant concerns. Additional meetings led to members identifying meaningful action items—a long list that included a personal narrative project. As you will see, the notion of the power of telling one's story was the impetus for this book.

I have read most of the essays and poems in Rick's manuscript multiple times. With each reading I go to a place of reflection that is well beyond wondering what it might be like to live with Parkinson's disease. Certainly he provides compelling descriptions of his experiences that are unique to having Parkinson's disease. But Rick's words also invite the reader to contemplate universal themes: the need for validation, the power and essential nature of living in the present, feeling deep loss, maintaining hope, struggling with identity. He does this with extraordinary skill—revealing his gifts as a writer, as a person who has been curious and reflective for most of his life, as a friend who seeks and offers support, and as one who can balance compassion with humor.

I am unaware of any book about Parkinson's disease like this one. Rick shares his understanding of PD from the perspective of one who has PD and with insight gained from tapping many resources to learn more about the disorder. Individuals with PD likely will relate to descriptions of that period when puzzling and frustrating and frightening symptoms went undiagnosed. Readers will be informed about some of the symptoms beyond tremors, freezing, and shuffling gait. Most of all, people will discover that Rick's distinctive story-telling and fresh, engaging writing will lift them to new considerations of this "degenerative process that chips away at the person I thought I was."

— Barbara Mathers-Schmidt, Ph.D., Professor and Chair, Department of Communication Sciences and Disorders, Western Washington University

Preface: Getting It Out of My Head

You may wonder why I wrote this book. I have asked myself the same question. Looking at my face in the mirror, I see the same guy I saw yesterday, who looks a lot like the guy I saw the day before that. I see the crooked smile, an angular head with twin lumps on either side of my upper forehead marking the insertion points of my deep-brain-stimulation electrodes. I see the slightly vacant, staring eyes. I know there's a brain in that head and that it's got some problems.

When James Parkinson wrote in 1817 about the shaking palsy, he described it mainly as a movement disorder, "the senses and intellects being uninjured." Living with Parkinson's disease over the course of the past 20 years, I've learned that the senses and intellects, in fact, take quite a beating.

It didn't occur to me to write a book, even a short one, about the experience of living with Parkinson's disease until I was encouraged by a positive response to the essay that became Chapter 2 of *Parkinson's Dreams about Me*. I wrote this book to explore and try to communicate what is happening to me as, with each passing year, the symptoms of Parkinson's disease grow worse. But I wanted to try writing it in a way that didn't necessarily follow the chronological progression of the disease. There is a section of the book, Part One, that tracks the disease progression chronologically, and other sections that move freely through space and time. Initially, and somewhat pre-sumptuously, I wanted my book to be unlike anyone else's Parkinson's book, as though I could somehow articulate what other people with Parkinson's don't already know about the disease.

For better or for worse, I think I got my wish. *Parkinson's Dreams about Me* isn't like anyone else's Parkinson's book, as far as I am aware. Now I see that just as all persons with Parkinson's (PWPs) have different flavors of the same dis-ease, I simply have a slightly different way of approaching the narrative.

There are many books, articles, blogs, personal web sites, Facebook pages, and who knows what other media that share personal stories of living with PD. Michael J. Fox wrote *Lucky Man* not long after publicly revealing that he had Parkinson's disease. His celebrity status is part of the appeal of his story, but under that layer is a certain order in which things occur, whether it's Michael J. Fox, my friend Mike, or anyone else with PD: early, undiag-nosed symptoms; stress from knowing that something is wrong; frustration with doctors who are trying to find out what might be wrong; finally, the diagnosis, which brings on emotions ranging from devastation to disbelief, anger to relief.

And that is just the beginning.

As our individual stories unfold, each one takes its unique shape. After 20 years with PD, at least this young-onset and once-young patient has a different perspective, as the early sense of what is possible has ever so slowly transformed into a compelling need to face the inevitable. At times, I feel simply worn out.

But it is significant that dancing, even while I am in the

grip of the symptoms of Parkinson's, has helped me find a way through periodic bouts of despair and exhaustion.

There are several poems at the end of the book. Since I am writing about my personal experience living with Parkinson's disease, I feel the poems show part of who I am, even though they are not really about Parkinson's disease. I am a PWP writing poems that come from a region identified as my life, trying to capture both the visible and the invisible. Poems are like voices that we most often choose not to listen to. When we listen, and feel, the resulting ability to self-express affects and enhances our connection to that invisible world, to the inner workings of identity.

Why I think I wrote this book is that I thought I had something distinct to say about the perception of how someone lives with Parkinson's disease. Or maybe I thought I had something familiar to say in a fresh and, I hope, engaging way. I held the reader's interests in mind as I wrote, but I also needed simply to get some this material out of my head. It needed a larger and more objective readership to determine whether or not I have shed any light on the nature of the illness, intertwined with strands of my autobiography, telling my stories to myself and to anyone who is listening.

Lastly, a word about date of diagnosis. PWPs often measure their time with PD by both the date of diagnosis as well as the date when symptoms were first noticed. My diagnosis was made in 1998, but in retrospect I can see that neurological symptoms began manifesting in 1992, shortly after a traffic accident that I will describe in the book.

Acknowledgments

I had no idea at the time this book was being written that a modest collection of essays, narratives, and poetry would require so much help from other people to come out with a published book. I have been rescued more than once from my own inefficiency and inability to keep a clear picture of where I was going and what I needed to do in order to get there. I have been encouraged to not give up, and I have been fortunate to receive help when it appeared there were not sufficient resources to proceed.

I want to acknowledge a few people upon whom I have relied—not only for their expertise, but for motivation and resolve.

Pam Kuntz, the founder and Artistic Director of Kuntz and Company, has been an inspiration to me during the few years I have known her. During that time, thanks to Pam, I've learned that I can dance. A choreographer, dancer, and teacher, Pam invited me to participate in a community-based production that included my first dance performance as a person with Parkinson's disease (PWP). We went on to develop a Dance for Parkinson's class that is in its second year, filling a need for Parkinson's patients to get out, move their bodies, learn about modern dance, meet new friends, and have fun. Pam believed in me as a dancer at a time when I had a very low estimation of my abilities and didn't feel up to being a local spokesperson for young-onset Parkinson's disease, much less dance. Pam is an artist who works intuitively and collaboratively, and her energy and choreographic style combine to create valuable and memorable works.

I would also like to thank Dr. Catherine Strong and Dr. Barbara Mathers-Schmidt for reading the manuscript, and for their support. Dr. Strong gave me practical advice to help me make the apparently complicated more simple. My deep thanks to Dr. Mathers-Schmidt for writing the book's foreword while running a university department, mentoring graduate students, and teaching courses, and for her compassionate enthusiasm and her love of interdisciplinary discourse and action.

I also gratefully acknowledge the efforts of Karen Cook, Joan Shul, and Kathleen Karella, who read and gave useful feedback on early versions of the manuscript.

My wife, Lee Willis, read chapters as they were written; she copyedited and made suggestions, which invariably improved the contents of the book. Barbara Gilday suggested I include poems, an idea that became a nice addition to the overall picture. Elizabeth Weber, trusted editor on my previous book, challenged me to make choices when I didn't want to make them. Liz generally encouraged me and convinced me that I had something valuable to say. Libby Lewis provided high-quality proofreading of the entire manuscript, which I deeply appreciate.

Even though it's been too long since we've talked, I want to thank Bill Bell, co-founder and former executive director of the Northwest Parkinson's Foundation in Seattle, for his leadership and warm humanity. The Foundation's office is in Seattle, and I live in Bellingham; if I have any sort of crisis, I know I can call Bill to meet for coffee at a Starbucks just north of Marysville, literally halfway.

Bill had a vision and a personal motivation to create an integrative center for Parkinson's disease patients that would address the whole person and not just an ailing *substantia nigra,* the walnut-sized part of the brain that plays an important role in movement. Bill had tried to find such care for his mother, who had lived with Parkinson's for many years, but discovered that there was nothing in the Puget Sound region that fit the need. So he and Craig Howard co-founded the Northwest Parkinson's Foundation. In 2000, the NWPF collaborated with Evergreen Healthcare to create the Booth Gardner Parkinson's Care Center at Evergreen Hospital in Kirkland, Washington, the facility where his mom received high-quality care until she passed away a short time ago.

Thank you also to the Northwest Parkinson's Foundation for publishing two articles of mine in the *Parkinson's Post* that have become, in slightly different form, the basis for two chapters in the present book.

Athlete, aerialist, surfer, expert at living life fully, Shannon Gray Collier has graciously allowed me to use personal material from private e-mail correspondence; this material can be found in Chapter 17, "The Tortoise and the Aerialist." I wish her a complete recovery from serious injuries sustained when she fell from the bar several feet above a concrete floor early in 2012.

To the members of my support group, Joan Suhl, Christine Englehart, Kathleen Karella, Dave Thomas, Jim Tolin, Sheila Hazel, Jeff Cotton, Karen Cook, and Barbara Mathers-Schmidt: Thank you all for listening, and thanks for your remarkable insights about living with Parkinson's disease.

Buckets of appreciation to the speech-language pathology

graduate students in the Department of Communication Sciences and Disorders, Western Washington University. May you all graduate with honors, and may each one of you find the job of your dreams.

A warm thank you to dear friends Jerry and Vivian Kelley, who know more than most of us about loss, for listening to me read the first two chapters one spring day in their living room in Lacey, Washington. I appreciate and value your support.

And a shout-out to my son Eli for saying, at a Christmas dinner as we went around the table sharing what we were grateful for, "I'm thankful that my dad is writing another book." That meant a lot to me. I needed to remember my own advice to believe in myself and in what I am doing.

To my family and friends, from whom I receive much love, support, and understanding: I do not take any of it for granted. These acts of love and support are not easily quantified but have helped keep me going during the sometimes fascinating, sometimes tedious, sometimes disheartening journey called Parkinson's disease, to say nothing of helping me to write a book about it.

Introduction

This collection of bite-size chapters containing my thoughts about living with Parkinson's disease is in no way a book about how to steer your own course through chronic illness. In fact, it would not be an exaggeration to say that there is very little in the way of "how-to" information regarding medications, neurosurgery, exercise, or any other Parkinson's-related topics. There are several good books and articles available to readers who seek professional medical information. A few of these are listed at the back of this book.

No treatment or procedure described herein or inferred from the book's content constitute medical advice. Talk to your doctor or medical team if you need help. I am neither a physician nor a magician. No tricks. Not many answers. I am only an expert in living with Parkinson's disease, speaking from the perspective of a 20-year veteran of PD.

There is no punch line. At the end, I don't become a Buddhist, clear and calm in my mind and body. I don't have an epiphanic reconciliation with the disease. I simply serve as witness to parts of my own story.

That said, I hope at least some of my thoughts, opinions, and emotions will help the reader with PD to feel less alone.

Living with Parkinson's disease is really a sort of continuing education program, in the course of which we concentrate on different aspects of the disease, like eager biology students with a formidable course load and a decreasing capacity to absorb, remember, and integrate new information.

I truly believe that anyone who lives with PD is an expert. The members of my support group in Bellingham are collectively a powerful resource: people telling their stories, bit by bit. We come back to the group because we know that we'll find honesty, trust, compassion, and true mutual understanding. It is a remarkable group, whose support and encouragement gave me the courage to even begin writing.

We are all graduate students in the movement disorders program, and telling our stories, in any form or manner, is one of the degree requirements.

Chapter 1, "The Tortoise with Parkinson's Disease," developed as I was thinking about an island in the ocean that I metaphorically inhabit. It was hard to resist the image of the stolid tortoise, who lumbered into my narrative and onto my island as a well-armored but slow-moving alter ego.

I actually know very little about tortoises. I learned from a recent *BBC News* report that a type of giant Galapagos tortoise believed extinct for 150 years probably still exists. That is good news because the tortoise population of the Galapagos was decimated in the 19th century by whalers on their forays into the Pacific Ocean. Unfortunately for the tortoises, they made an ideal food stock for whaling ships, as they can go without food for months. Thus they provided a source of fresh meat whenever the captain decided to kill them. Not only that; as the article goes on to explain, "The animals are thought to have colonised the archipelago through floating from the shores of South America."

The giant tortoises floated from mainland South America to the Galapagos Islands? That's a distance of more than five hundred miles. Why on earth would they do that? Were things so awful in Chile that they just floated away? Did they know that there were islands out there?

The answer is a secret. Tortoises are good at keeping secrets.

I am not a war correspondent, but these pages comprise the reports that I have brought back from the trenches, my ideas and opinions about PD and related topics. I realized as I wrote these pieces that I really don't know more about Parkinson's disease than anyone else with PD. I'm just telling stories from my life, trying to say something about the way this person with Parkinson's disease thinks and what his life is like. The chapters are like pieces of a puzzle that I am working on, late at night, in the darkness when I can't roll over in bed, when it's just me and the disease.

My philosophical acumen has grown dusty since my days at the university when I read Anselm of Canterbury, Saint Thomas Aquinas, René Descartes, and other philosophers struggling valiantly with the ontological argument for the existence of God. The writing herein is both narrative and philosophical in nature. It is primarily a collection of stories from my life as they relate to having Parkinson's.

In fact, I travel in this book from the existential question, "Who am I?" (or, as a teacher once posed the question, "Who am I if I'm not struggling?") to the seemingly narcissistic inquiry, "What do other people think about me?" These are stories and essays that describe my relationship to depression, to novels and movies, to friends, to assistance dogs, to God, to my son, to my wife of 27 years, to the spirits of dead horses, and to the life of a tortoise, to name a few. Some of the incidents in the pieces presented here happened 30 years ago. Some happened yesterday.

Following a diagnosis of parkinsonism, one thing students of PD discover early on is that Parkinson's disease medications are not only very powerful drug compounds; they are also extremely expensive. Prices seem to be climbing as fast as college tuition. Those with chronic disease can count on needing and paying for these medications over the long haul. I wouldn't be here without them, so I'm glad they are available.

But as we move into the pharmacology portion of the syllabus, we begin to wonder (at least I do): Where is all this money going? I don't know. Let's make that a separate course. As I write, however, I am aware that I am benefiting from the Bush administration's implementation of Medicare Part D for partial coverage of the cost of medication for the disabled and elderly. President Obama's health care program also seeks to shrink the financial burden to recipients of Medicare Part D during the noncoverage period popularly referred to as the "doughnut hole."

Granted, there are some good new and improved pharmaceutical options for keeping Parkinson's symptoms in check, as well as novel delivery modalities such as the Neupro (rotigotine) transdermal dopamine agonist patch, and the continuous duodenal infusion of L-dopa directly into the digestive tract. More recently, markers used in conjunction with advanced imaging techniques are showing promise for image-based diagnosis.

There is the deep brain stimulation (DBS) surgical option, which is allowing some of us to continue to function. Nationally we can boast of Parkinson's "Centers of Excellence" at major research hospitals and clinical facilities that employ movement disorder specialists and a host of adjunctive therapists for body and mind, all focused on improving the quality of life for people with Parkinson's disease.

But I don't really hear much about progress in treating the disease itself.

Science is a slow-moving ship, and it takes a long time to make course adjustments. The silence about major breakthroughs in research is perhaps something we have to live with.

Still, the slow speed of progress is frustrating.

When it comes, the "cure" for Parkinson's disease is not going to be simple, in my opinion. I suspect that it will be a complicated, iterative, and expensive process. It will probably not work for everyone and may have a negative impact on other parts of the brain and body.

I hope I'm wrong.

artwork by Ruthie V

PART ONE

My Parkinson's Disease Chronology

The years pass like so many dry leaves scattered helter-skelter by an autumn breeze. One after another, 20 years have passed since the first signs that something was very wrong in my body and in my brain.

Everything has to start somewhere. It has been said that time is what keeps everything from happening all at once. Maybe that is why I have trouble with chronological narrative; my brain no longer works as a linear timeline.

There are many theories about the nature of time—the relationship between past, present, and future; what gives time its direction; time's role in causality and circularity; and how "time" is related to the mind. I know I am not without company in questioning how time "works."

And yet, here I have attempted to describe the path I have taken with Parkinson's from 1992 to the present.

I know that I am changing through time, being remolded as Parkinson's does its work on my body and mind. A degenerative process chips away at the person I thought I was. In recent years I've come to live more in the present, because outside of the moment lies chaos and uncertainty. The real world, based on the anticipation of what is to be and the memory of that which has passed, and which I no longer believe to be solid ground, likes a straight line.

Here it is, then, almost straight.

January 1992 (via 1972)

I had been riding a bike as transportation since college. When I left Washington State University (WSU) in January 1972, I had to leave behind my bike—a yellow Schwinn Le Tour—because I was flying directly to Mexico. I returned for it in June, my plan being to ride it back to Seattle, where I was taking up residence.

It was a beautiful early-summer day as I pedaled uphill and out of town. I could hear the birds singing. I waved and smiled at people who were retrieving the morning edition of the *Spokesman Review* from their mailboxes on the edge of the two-lane road that dropped and climbed and dropped again, following the contours of the hilly landscape, bright green with new growth of this year's wheat crop. I experienced a feeling of lightness and joy in the repetitive action of my legs propelling me through this beautiful morning in the country called the Palouse.

Of course, because I hadn't yet experienced time's circularity or one-pointedness, I had no premonition that just about 20 years after this memorable but ultimately exhausting ride, I would be hit and knocked off my bike by a car, T-boned as I bicycled to work on a dark, rainy morning, in heavy traffic on the first day of winter quarter classes at Western Washington University in Bellingham.

I could see and feel the impact in slow motion as I separated from my bike, bounced off the car's windshield, and blacked out, coming back into my body squatting in the middle of the street, my helmet intact but my bike wrecked. I was in shock, to the extent that I asked the person who hit me to take me to work, which she, doubtless in shock as well, agreed to do. My colleagues took one look at me, and one of them gave me a ride home, because I was obviously not able to perform any work.

No bones had been broken, and I had been wearing a helmet. I don't remember whether my helmet struck the pavement.

There is disagreement—or maybe just a lack of enough research data—in the Parkinson's medical community about the connection between brain trauma and Parkinson's disease. Is there a causal relationship? Can trauma or injury to the head trigger neurological changes that lead to some of the degenerative pathologies associated with neurological diseases such as Parkinson's?

March 1992

My family doctor of many years, Dick McClenahan, had been working with me to provide relief from anxiety and depression. It wasn't helping much. But I had to do something about the situation, because my depression was eroding my marriage, leaving me at a turning point: Get help, or lose my family. Dick said some of his patients had been experiencing good results from a relatively new class of antidepressant medication, the selective serotonin reuptake inhibitors (SSRIs), which includes Prozac, Paxil,

Zoloft and Lexapro. I agreed to try Prozac, which was at the time the most popular mood-enhancing antidepressant on the market. He wrote me a prescription intended to titrate my dose up to a therapeutic level, and said to call him if I had any problems. (What kind of problems? I wondered.)

This was only a couple of months after my bike accident. I had taken some time away from work and returned part-time and somewhat tentatively, traveling on foot and by city bus rather than bicycle. Walking to the bus stop one day, I had my first full-blown panic attack: sweating, dizziness, thumping heartbeat, speechlessness, fear, thinking I was going to die. By the time I got home, I was in better shape, and it occurred to me that I had been taking Prozac for a week. I called McClenahan's office and told Dick about my experience. I had a sense that it was a reaction to Prozac, but I'll never know for sure because I told Dick I was going to quit taking it. It would be months before I had the courage to give another SSRI, Paxil, a chance, which I did because my depression wasn't getting any better.

A few days after the panic attack, I began experiencing vague neurological symptoms: weakness, random areas of numbness in my arms and legs, disorientation and confusion, forgetfulness. My handwriting and typing had become less accurate, like my fingers wouldn't cooperate. But I didn't think much about it at that time. Looking back, I regard these as early symptoms of Parkinson's disease.

1992 – 1995

This period is a vague blur in my memory, and the vagueness is linked to the stress I felt about the unexplained neurological symptoms I was experiencing in addition to my worsening depression. Depression is its own lover—it just keeps recreating itself, and the pleasure it takes in causing pain to its host is part of the illness.

During those months and years, I went to work and was the dependable Rick Hermann, liked by most of the staff, managers, and directors because I did my job well and wore a bright face to go along with my can-do attitude. I began traveling for business, attending conferences and trade shows in my company's area of high-technology expertise, as well as scholarly publishing seminars and conferences. My wife and son frequently accompanied me on these junkets, to places such as San Francisco, Orlando, San Diego, San Jose, and Hawaii. When they didn't accompany me, I did fine on my own. When I came home, however, I always reverted to a depressed, angry state. My wife—I don't know how she managed to stay with me—couldn't deal with my dysfunction. I tried counseling, exercise and dietary regimens, homeopathic remedies, meditation, naturopathy, vitamin B_{12} shots, and anything I came across that wasn't a mainstream pharmacological product. Many of these measures I tried seemed to make me feel a little better for a day or two, but the effect, if any, was fleeting; inevitably, I would lose hope and spiral downward.

I may never know the impact of my depression on our son as he was growing up, but I think my depressive anger was directed more at my wife. I tried on some level to be a good dad. In the process I learned that a boy needs to have not just a father but other positive male role models and mentors in his life; it takes a village to raise a child, and it takes more than a father and mother alone to raise a son.

Dick McClenahan suggested on more than one occasion that some of my neurological symptoms could result from my sensitivity to small changes in my body, and that my overactive body awareness, could be a result of chronic depression. I maintained stubbornly that depression had nothing to do with my symptoms. They were "real," and I could not see this any other way.

As it turned out, I was right about the symptoms not being purely psychosomatic, but I was wrong in concluding that my depression could be cured without medical and psychiatric intervention. Antidepressant medications were and are a life-saving tool for me. I might not be here today if I didn't have access to them. I'll tell you what I think right now: if given a choice between living with either Parkinson's disease or chronic depression, I'd go with the Parkinson's.

Finally, in 1995, I went for a neurological exam at Dick McClenahan's urging. The neurologist was a young doctor, a nice guy whose name I can't remember. He did a thorough clinical examination, taking voluminous, neatly written notes that documented my condition beautifully.

He didn't have a clue what was wrong with me.

1996 – 1998

I'm slow, but I'm no dummy. In the nineties, as the Internet took over our lives like some wonky virus, amateur medical research and information sharing had become rampant. So that's where I went with my bagful of symptoms in hand. I researched neurological disorders on the Internet and suspected that I had Parkinson's disease. I by no means thought of my hunch as a substitute for a medical diagnosis, but close enough to turn the hunch into an educated guess. I was losing my ability to use a computer keyboard, and voice-recognition technology was marooned on a desert island that no one seemed to care about. I was told by human resources that the company would get me any available tools that I needed to help me type, but there are no tools for an employee with Parkinson's who needs to type an important document on the fly. I was dragging my right leg at this point, and occasionally stutter-stepping in a way that presaged gait freezing that would become an everyday part of my life a few years later.

I remember doing the stutter step as I passed through the door while entering my boss's office. "Are you okay?" he asked.

"Yeah, I'm fine," I lied.

The best thing that happened during this stretch was that I began a course of the SSRI antidepressant drug Paxil and had very good results. In fact, the effect was textbook perfect: after a 30-day course, I began making jokes, feeling much lighter, and was able to make choices about how I reacted to whatever came at me. I was saved! It was a remarkable transformation. I felt good in a way I could barely remember. My friends all said, "It's like the real Rick is back." I took Paxil on a continuous basis until 2010, when I switched to a different medication because the benefits of Paxil were getting smaller.

At some point, I sought the advice of another neurologist, Dr. Patrick Delaney, a stroke specialist from St. Louis. I liked Pat, and we enjoyed a measure of lighthearted conversation whenever I came in for an exam. Our bantering might not have been totally appropriate for an office dedicated to trying to diagnose which particular type of degen-erative brain disorder the patient is presenting. But it calmed my nerves and made me feel like a person, not like a medical chart with a name on it.

Pat ordered an MRI scan of my brain. As a stroke guy, he was an expert at diagnosing all things stroke-related. This is simply to say, without criticism, that when you're a hammer, everything has a greater tendency to look like a nail. On one slice of my MRI scan he noticed a small blank area, a lacuna, which he interpreted—diagnosed—as a silent lacunar infarction, a "silent" stroke that may not even be noticed by the patient, but which tends to recur, sometimes with cognitive and motor difficulties that are progressively disabling.

Lacunar infarcts can be preceded by transient ischemic attacks (TIAs), or mini-strokes. I had no recollection of experiencing such an event or events. If my lacuna was real, the prognosis was poor, because, while silent lacunar infarcts can create a kind of parkinsonism with cognitive involvement, the standard Parkinson's medications have minimal to no effect on the symptoms.

I never really "believed in" this stroke diagnosis. I had no risk factors, no family history of stroke, no high blood pressure, nor other markers pointing toward the diagnostic best-guess I had been given. I wanted a second opinion, and Pat Delaney encouraged me to have other experts read the MRI. So I made an appointment with a neurologist in Seattle. He could not confirm the existence of a lacuna on my brain scan. Neither could the chief of radiology at a large hospital with excellent neurology and imaging resources. So I still didn't know what I "had," aside from my aforementioned hunch.

A resting tremor that developed in my right arm in early 1998 saved me from further anxiety about a diagnosis, or lack thereof. I was already presenting with reduced arm swing on my right side, micrographia, right-leg drag, deep fatigue, some postural instability, and "cogwheel-effect" limb rigidity. The resting tremor sealed the deal on a clinical diagnosis of parkinsonism, delivered by Pat Delaney at some point during 1998. I don't recall the date specifically, because in a sense I had been fairly sure that what I had was idiopathic Parkinson's disease (see Glossary). My response to the diagnosis was great relief. What I had been struggling with for over five years finally had a name.

Even better, there were medications and surgical options available that meant I could continue to lead a relatively normal life. I soon learned the truism that you don't die of Parkinson's; you live with it. But it was a somewhat hollow reassurance that I needn't anticipate an "early" death, as if Death could ever be considered "late."

Now, I didn't know at the time that parkinsonism could take different forms—not only the kind of Parkinson's disease most people with parkinsonism, including me, are faced with, but also the so-called Parkinson's Plus syndromes, such as progressive supranuclear palsy (PSP), multiple-system atrophy (MSA), and vascular parkinsonism, all of which spell a relatively fast, devastating disease course leading to death. I have always thought that the term "Parkinson's Plus" implies a bonus of some kind. It is sadly no joke for the patient stricken with one of these monstrous disorders, nor is it in any way easy for families and close friends to come to terms with such a diagnosis.

1999 – 2001

In 1999 I told my employer that I had Parkinson's disease. The organization was very supportive but perhaps somewhat confused. At the time, another employee had been diagnosed with multiple sclerosis involving peripheral neuropathy, and she was in a wheelchair. I was getting good results from my Parkinson's medications, so I wasn't in a wheelchair.

It was a period in which I had a lot of internal churning about just how disabled I was at the time, or how disabled I might become, wanting to maintain a "normal" appearance and a high level of competency in my job performance. I was soon to discover the reality of the disease's own progressively disabling agenda. But until that realization came, I felt as if I almost had to convince people that I was sick, which in turned made me examine my own beliefs about the qualities that comprise illness and ask myself if I in fact qualified. It was a strange way to look at my situation.

My job performance began to be impacted and change subtly. For example, I found myself spending more time on the phone talking to authors whose books I wanted my organization to publish. There was nothing inherently wrong with this; it is an important part of acquiring books—one is compelled to gain the trust of the author and to act on the basis of that trust. I found it relatively easy to do phone work, or to converse face to face with people at conferences. As long as I was in the moment, talking, I was articulate but not garrulous, sensitive to the unwritten protocol informing the author-editor relationship, and respectful of the authors' standing in the scientific and engineering communities.

Once I got off the phone, however, I found it hard to do any kind of follow-up, to log information gained from the conversation, or to make a plan, to budget the project, and to create a schedule that worked within the context of available editorial and production resources.

As I would learn in workshops and from neurologists, my experience most likely had to do with loss or impairment of so-called executive functions (see Glossary) of my brain. A certain percentage of people with PD experience executive function disorder, and I was one of them.

My decision to let management know that I had been diagnosed with Parkinson's disease was in a sense a pre-emptive action—although I didn't think of it in those terms at the time—that gave me a feeling I was in control of my own fate to some extent.

I imagined that I would work for several more years, given the great response I was having to Sinemet (see Glossary).

Still, I felt uneasy that other employees, including my immediate supervisor, didn't really understand what was wrong. Could it be that the severity of my symptoms is always more noticeable to me than it is to others?

In 2001, I thought I had four, maybe five more years of being able to work, but only lasted one, even after cutting my schedule by 50 percent. I was barely able to find the energy for half-time employment and became exhausted with the effort those four hours of daily work demanded.

2002 – 2005

I left my job and career in May 2002 and stepped into my new life, which resembled my old life to the extent that I was still me. I applied for Social Security and Medicare. From all of the problems many people report in dealing with the government bureaucracy, I was for some reason spared the inconvenience and the usual delays and appeals, a process that can go on for years. Every government employee with whom I had contact during this part of the process was helpful, respectful, and, so far as I could determine, kind.

The week after I actually walked out of my office building for the last time, I underwent foot surgery unrelated to PD, and my mother died unexpectedly. A lot was changing, but leaving work was the right thing to do. I never went back to visit because I didn't want to be a "former employee." I wanted to live my life. While I believe that I was well-regarded at my job, and that colleagues were friends as well as co-workers, I learned a lesson from our parting of ways: people with whom you interact in a working environment on a daily basis are not necessarily friends. Most of them are really nice people, and as long as work has to be done, the best way to make it easier is to create a network of support comprising your "friends." Once you are no longer part of the team, that particular social contract expires.

There are no bad feelings, and I have in fact retained a couple of acquaintances from work well after my retirement. We have dinner or drink beer and talk every few months. It's just the way things go.

I don't think other people in the organization really knew what was wrong with me. Most of the time I felt "normal," and my symptoms were probably unnoticeable to anyone merely looking at me. Particularly surreal was my "retirement" office party. I'm sure I seemed fine and that people wondered, "What's wrong with this guy?" At the party, an outdoor barbecue that took place around 11:00 in the morning, the sun shining benignly upon the well-wishers and me, there were all the trappings of a typical good-bye bash. Especially notable were the joke cards and thoughtful gifts and good food that had become de rigueur for a farewell celebration. I had been to several such gatherings in honor of someone moving on to a better job, or going back to school for a master's degree, or actually retiring because the employee had reached retirement age. And me? I was going on Social Security and Medicare. It was the weirdest party I have ever been to. I'm sure that most present wished me well—at whatever it was I was going to do.

Although nearly 150 people were employed where I worked, I have only seldom seen any of them around town subsequent to my departure. It doesn't seem that Bellingham is big enough to swallow that number of former co-workers. But our regimented orbits keep us in the equivalent of different solar systems.

Life was better after I stopped working. I wasn't constantly getting stressed and fatigued trying to perform work I could no longer do. Consequently, some of my Parkinson's symptoms eased or leveled off for a few months. PD became just something that was always in the shadows, waiting to make another advance.

For the next couple of years, I hung out. I began writing songs and, realizing that Parkinson's was slowly but surely taking my fingers hostage, I asked my brother to record me playing the guitar and singing the songs I had written.

I had a sense of wanting to leave something that I had created that would be out in the world when I no longer am.

The question I had the most trouble answering during these early years was one that people asked a lot: "What do you do with your time?"

Hmm. Time again.

I rarely had an answer that was very compelling, finally settling for a positive but noncommittal standard response: "I'm staying as active as possible." Which was true. I took yoga and tai chi classes, rode a horse, still did some bicycling, lifted weights at the senior activity center, and walked. One activity that I had absolutely loved was riding a longboard (a skateboard designed for downhill and slalom street riding). More out of an instinct for self-preservation than a sense of actual responsibility, I sold my last board at a garage sale a few years ago, gave my helmet to a neighborhood kid, and at least as a skater bid adieu to the hilly streets of Bellingham, especially the ones in new housing developments where the asphalt was still smooth and fast.

On the next block over from ours lived a half-dozen moms with kids ages newborn to three. Dads lived there too, but they were off at work all day. So I wandered over to Grant Street one summer morning and decided that this group of moms and kids would become my social network for at least the near future. As the summer wore on, I played games with the kids, walked the dogs, and had coffee and discussed child-rearing books with the moms.

My own son Eli graduated from high school in 2004, and in the fall of that year he left for the University of Montana in Missoula, where he fell in love with wilderness camping and fly fishing, while maintaining a decent grade point and managing to practice and compete on the Grizzlies' cross-country and track teams.

The yard and house maintenance became a burden for me because of Parkinson's disease. Lee and I had been looking at condominiums in Bellingham for a year or so, and it just happened that the one we had been watching suddenly became available just after Eli started his freshman year at UM. We jumped on the condo and were moved out of our house of 16 years by Thanksgiving. Eli was surprised that we had actually moved to a condo, but when he came home for the holiday, his assessment was that it was sort of like the old house. He liked it. Lee and I breathed a sigh of relief.

2006 – 2007

For my 56th birthday, on March 9, 2007, I received two surprises. One was that my son showed up unexpectedly at the door, having flown in from Missoula for my birthday. The other, which had been organized by my wife so secretively that I had no clue, was a surprise birthday party for me. It was all set up at the condo association's clubhouse.

Weeks earlier, she had given copies of a CD containing songs I had written and performed, and which had been recorded by my brother Ron, to several musicians I know. She asked that each choose a song to perform at the birthday party. I was overwhelmed when I walked in and found the people who were most important to me, then sat in the front row and listened to my friends sing the songs I'd written over the previous three years.

And yet, there was a funereal undertone to the evening, almost as if people were saying goodbye to me. In a sense, they were saying goodbye to a part of me, the part no longer capable of performing these songs myself. My gratitude for these friends was mixed with a melancholy note. My birthday celebration was the end of one world, as well as the birth of a new reality that would accompany me for all the years to come.

Around the time I was piecing together *Mothers and Babies,* my CD of original songs, I also began to consider deep-brain stimulation (DBS) surgery. It was a challenge to the ascendancy of Parkinson's disease, which seemed to be progressively taking over more of my life. As I was to discover, Parkinson's is not so easily rattled.

My neurology team had encouraged me to give this option serious and prompt consideration because there is a window of time in the progression of the disease that makes a positive outcome more likely. I was in that window.

I was not completely reconciled, however, with the surgical approach. Every PD case is unique in the way a patient responds to pharmaceutical or surgical interventions, and I had long held that surgery be considered as a last option. Surgeons, even neurosurgeons, love doing surgery. I'm happy for that. But, as I have found the general case to be, surgeons aren't as interested in post-op care of the patient except as it relates to the foot, kidney, tumor, or brain they have surgically altered. That's fine; I'm glad they do what they do, and that they are proficient and that we have such finely targeted surgical specialties, especially in neurosurgery. I didn't need to be reminded that DBS is brain surgery. Risks, though infrequent, include stroke, bleeding, infection, and death.

2008

I considered the DBS option for the better part of a year. I became proficient at arguing pros and cons in my head, citing uncertainties and possible near-miraculous outcomes. But I was blocked somewhere and could not consciously make a decision.

Then, one day in March, which I recall as sunny with a cool breeze blowing in from Bellingham Bay, while I was walking down the street, I realized clearly that my life with Parkinson's disease was not going in the right direction. In that moment of clarity I knew that I had to try the DBS surgery. It was the only game out there that might help me buy some time while better and more effective products, medications, and disease-altering approaches could be developed. I needed to stay out in front of the advance of symptoms, although, as with medications, DBS does nothing to stop disease progression.

I was scheduled for surgery in July. As it turned out, I had two operations: one to open my brain and insert electrodes into my subthalmic nucleus, and another to implant two Medtronic battery packs, one on each side of my chest, just below my collarbones. The batteries connect to the electrodes via subcutaneous wires at the insertion point for the electrodes just at the top of my forehead. At the junctions, it looks like I have antler buds.

The surgery itself was successful. The critical-care staff members were outstanding. I was in their care overnight, then shipped down to the general population, ostensibly for another day and night of recovery time. The contrast between the floor staff and the critical care people was enormous. Let me say that I am grateful for all the medical care I have received, thanks to Medicare and its providers. I am not knocking hospital care, but I understood then how one must take care of oneself as a patient in a hospital. Having said that, I can't help but recall the lack of good communication between me and the over-extended nursing staff during even my first hour in a convalescent room. I had to ask a friend who is an MD and who lived nearby to help get me out of there. An hour and a half after being wheeled into the room, I was walking out, much to the consternation of the floor chief RN.

Thus ended the first phase of my DBS experience. The hardware was in place. My brain was given a month to recover from the trauma of surgery before being subjected to programming. My neurologist told me that programming could take a few months to get the right settings.

It ended up taking a year.

During my post-op month and before the stimulation was even turned on, there was a sense of impatience and anticipation moderated by the neurology team's reminders that I shouldn't hope for too much too soon. Surgery turned out to be the easy part.

As a patient, I found the programming process fascinating but absolutely draining. For the first appointment, at which the programmer and neurologist worked together to calibrate my settings, I was told to come into the office in an *off* state (see Glossary) without taking my usual medications. This allowed the team to get a truer feeling for which changes were due to medication and which to stimulation.

I was not moving very well when I arrived for the session. The programmer hooked her control device to the impulse generators on the left side of my chest (she would do each side separately) and activated certain electrode frequencies and power output levels that made my right leg begin tremoring wildly, to the degree that everybody in the room had to quickly get out of the way. The same thing happened with my other leg, my arms, my head. One setting made my speech slur so that I could barely talk. Although I was not "doing" anything, much was being done with me. It was wild. That first session lasted four hours— longer than the brain surgery itself.

I was exhausted. At one point, the programmer turned the stimulation to zero, and I still hadn't taken any medication. As the DBS system powered down, my brain was screaming for dopamine. Completely and literally off, I was in an elevator going down to the bottom basement floor where no part of me moved. I was unable to open my eyes, and it felt like nothing. It was like being dead.

2009

After almost a year of adjusting my stimulation programing, the DBS results were poorer than hoped for. When DBS surgery makes it possible for the patient to run on fewer medications taken less frequently, or even to not need medication at all for a year or two, that is considered hitting a home run. My results were more like hitting an infield single. However, the fact is DBS can only make you feel as good as you did on your best day prior to stimulation. By that measure, although we tried and were unable to decrease my medication levels, I can hardly complain.

I am very thankful for the benefits I did get from the DBS process. Primarily, my *dyskinesias* (see Glossary) had abated substantially. People in my yoga class remarked on how much better I was. I wasn't moving and wiggling around. Even though that uncontrolled movement was more a side-effect of Parkinson's medications than the disease itself, I'll take it.

Good DBS programmers have to be both intuitive artists as well as objective scientists. I can't begin to understand how they have even a remote chance of finding the right settings to have a therapeutic effect without sending the patient into a frenzy of over-stimulation.

They are working with four electrodes on each side of the brain, attached to two separate leads inserted through holes drilled into the skull. The electrodes are positioned at different depths in the subthalmic nucleus. (Some DBS patients have only one side of the brain stimulated.) It's similar to long-line fishing in which baited hooks attached by leaders to the main line are set at varying levels above the sea bottom, depending on which kind of fish the long-liner is trying to catch.

Each of the eight electrodes can be set to pulse at various frequencies and stimulation levels, creating what seems to me a phenomenal number of choices and combinations. This must drive programmers up the wall.

The physician's assistant who did my initial programming and tweaked it for a year finally said, "Rick, I'm sorry. I've tried everything I know that has worked on other patients. I don't have anything more beneficial to offer, beyond what you've already got."

That's how it goes in using new technologies. Every PD patient is a different person who responds to treatment in a unique manner.

Deep-brain stimulation, as my neurosurgeon likes to say, is a bridge technology to keep PWPs as highly functional as possible until The Next Great Thing comes along. It feels to me like DBS is a trapeze artist high above the crowd. She has let go of her own bar and now flies in midair, confident that her partner hanging from another bar and swinging in her direction will catch her.

People with Parkinson's disease who have undergone DBS surgery are waiting to see what, if anything, is ahead of us that will have significant impact on disease progression.

2010

My sister died of cancer in April, and one of the things that she had encouraged me to do was to finish a story I was writing. I had not written short fiction for more than 30 years. (My character's name is Old Major Tom Keenan, and I did not know of David Bowie's song "Calling Major Tom" until another Tom—Tom Jones, but not *that* Tom Jones— pointed out the connection.) I finished writing "The Bright World of Dandelion Court" and went on to write eight or nine other new stories, added four older ones written and published when I was in my twenties. It is my first book, self-published, a volume of short fiction named after that story my sister encouraged me to finish: *The Bright World of Dandelion Court: stories and other lies.* In the short story collection, Parkinson's disease and neurological dysfunction are part of what many of the characters must face: a mom with MS; a misshapen, not altogether reliable dwarf who is losing his short-term memory; and a young man with PD who falls in love with one of his hallucinations. Like the character losing his memory, the closer I get to the present in this chronology, the fewer memories I seem to have.

Bookending 18 years with Parkinson's disease, I was hit by a pickup truck that knocked me off my recumbent trike in March 2010. As in 1992, nothing was obviously broken, but I was shaken up enough to see that bicycling on the streets of Bellingham was no longer for me. I sold the trike. The cars had won. Now I take the bus, which isn't so bad. Or I walk. Which is a good thing.

2011

This was the year of dance and becoming locally "famous." Several events and opportunities came together. The book came out and got a favorable review. I helped to organize and promote a class somewhat awkwardly but accurately called Dance for People with Parkinson's Disease and Other Neurological and Movement Disorders. Pam Kuntz, a creative dancer and choreographer I'd come to know and become friends with, taught the first class in the fall of 2010, and as of April 2012 the class is still going strong—has in fact grown to two classes a week. I love all the people I've come to know, and sometimes have had the honor to work with, in the Bellingham modern dance community. As I said in a news video produced by a Seattle network affiliate about Parkinson's disease and dance, "I thought dancing was something other people did."

I *freeze* (see Glossary) a lot more, have fallen a few times, and feel the effects of wear and tear of the disease in my lowered energy level and mood. At times, I hate this disease. Other times, I don't mind.

2012

I turned 61 this March.

It has been a dark winter, both Lee and I getting on with our lives, staying "active" and connected to the world through classes, exercise, friends, volunteer work, and other ways of reaching out.

Only this year have I begun to gain an awareness of my reluctance to travel. Travel is an American obsession, and in my 20s and 30s I was a willing and enthusiastic traveler. Today, walking the trails of the park beyond my back door (where most of my more durable ideas originate), I reflect on how the traveling metaphor has long been used to describe a life path, a quest, an adventure taken by the soul, an evolutionary journey out of the darkness.

This is something different than travel according to the routes and activity opportunities described in travel books, but spiritual inquiry is not necessarily inconsistent with worldly adventure.

For me, unfortunately, travel has become a near-phobia. I haven't stepped onto an airplane since 9/11. Part of this travel aversion is due to Parkinson's disease, and the prospect of managing routines, medications, and other regimens while on the road. Only recently have I begun to see this aversion as a dysfunction that goes beyond having PD, one that puts limitations on my participation in life.

As I conclude this narrative, I am aware that it does not end. After 20 years of living with Parkinson's disease, I am still learning about it, getting uncomfortably familiar with its needs, and developing a firm conviction that I require something better than hope. I need courage, true grit, and evidence that research is leading in the right direction. And I need my family and friends, and faith in something I am unable to call by name or fully comprehend.

photo by Lee Willis

PART TWO

Living with Parkinson's Disease

1.

The Tortoise with Parkinson's Disease

My usual state of consciousness is not a state at all. It is an island in the middle of the ocean, protected by a barrier reef. In the lagoon between the reef and the island, colorful tropical fish swim through clear water, which meets the island's shore at an undisturbed white sand beach. The ocean beyond the reef holds all of the terror, shame, guilt, rotting memories, and dangerous thoughts and feelings that once lived inside me and that I have long since banished from the island.

The island is my residence, my safe haven. However, I have discovered that the reef is permeable, with hidden deep-water passages through which monsters can squeeze, undetected until they creep from the lagoon water at night like slippery amphibians, and find me in sleep as nightmares.

I don't dream about Parkinson's disease. Sometimes I think that Parkinson's dreams about me. Maybe even dreams me into existence, making me confront my shadow self.

The nightmares are like seismic activity foretelling a catastrophic event, perhaps an earthquake in some deep canyon closer to the earth's core, and then a devastating tsunami. I have no idea when it will hit, but it will be fast and unexpected.

I think I reached a tipping point this year. For one thing, I finally refused to take a new medication prescribed by my neurologist. I felt like it was just another endless list of side-effects and dietary restrictions, and you know what? I'm tired. I just don't want to take more pills than I already take. I have to tell my neurologist about this. Maybe next week.

I used to appreciate pills. I got to know them, their different shapes, sizes, and colors. I still appreciate my symptom-relieving medications, and I hate them as well. I am certain that if there is a "cures Parkinson's" pill, the list of side-effects and contra-indications would look something like this: "Caution, this medication may cause liver damage, hypertension, hallucinations, suicidal thoughts, vascular parkinsonism, and death."

Is that what we are waiting for?

Most nights, my dreams and nightmares are flattened by the anti-anxiety medications I take. I am more afraid of losing my island than of dying.

So, my island.

I sometimes wonder who in their right mind would ever want to explore the ocean beyond the coral reef. Monsters lurk there, deep and venomous. Millions of years ago, it wasn't like this. Before consciousness the ocean was free of anger, shame, hate, and guilt. Of love, too.

It was nothing at all.

On my island, which is not in the Galapagos archipelago, there is a beach preserve set aside specifically for tortoises who lay their eggs in the warm white sand. Many of the tortoises that frequent the island have lived longer than I have been alive.

In the fable of the tortoise and the hare, as in nature, the tortoise is, quite frankly, slow. That is part of its evolutionary path. It relies on qualities other than speed to survive.

Interestingly enough, one of the cardinal symptoms of Parkinson's disease is bradykinesia, a fancy way of saying that PWPs move like tortoises on terra firma. Slowly. Parkinson's is not a condition that is defined only by rhythmic tremor or uncontrollable dyskinesias. Parkinson's disease, in fact, is the progressive loss of the ability to move at all. Realizing that I am losing speed makes me identify with the tortoise.

I'm not sure slow and steady will win this race.

2.

Who Am I?
Parkinson's Disease As Spiritual Inquiry

When you see a friend or someone with whom you have a casual acquaintance, that person doesn't generally walk up to you and ask, "Who *are* you?" No. The question you are asked is, "*How* are you?" And you say fine or good or okay. Maybe you provide some additional information, such as, "Not great today; yesterday was better." But what would we say if someone did ask us *who* we are?

Another scenario: A new acquaintance, maybe someone you meet at a party, asks innocently, "So, what do you do?" Which most likely means, what is your function in the economy? That's a tough one if you're no longer working because you've been struggling with Parkinson's disease. So, if you give that information to the person who has asked the question, the next inquiry, still meant as a pleasant if somewhat uncertain session of "getting to know you," might be, "Well, what do you do with all that spare time?"

As a person with Parkinson's disease, I sometimes don't have an answer. So I fumble around in my brain and often admit that I can't remember anything I've done recently, but that I have managed to stay busy doing … something.

When I worked, I was very on top of everything I did every day. When I could no longer assemble the faculties

I needed to do my job, it was the beginning of the end for my employment as an editor, a career that I truly enjoyed.

I learned early on that this memory sieve reflects a loss of the brain's executive functions. Because I was never an executive, I had no idea I had any function to lose. Neurologically speaking, the loss or impairment of executive functions refers to loss of the brain's ability to do task-switching, planning, scheduling, recognizing possible consequences of current actions, making sound judgments, and even following directions. Thirty years ago I worked as a professional chef and caterer. Now I break into a cold sweat when I contemplate a recipe with more than three ingredients and few steps.

Impairment of executive functioning has cognitive impact as well, involving the frontal cortex in particular. It gets complicated after that, involving a web of neural equations that I can't begin to solve.

Back to who I am. I have been thinking lately that I should spend less time trying to be someone I once was, or someone I'm not, and practice being who I am. The problem is, I sometimes can't say who I am. What I write or think about today, or whatever aspect of my life I identify with this week, seems to have no connection to where I was two weeks ago. Nor will it likely reveal the same "self" two weeks from now. Early on in my life with Parkinson's I talked glibly about constantly adjusting to the "new normal." It was a concept I could understand, because it felt as if every week my brain dug into a new fortified position that might repel attack for a few days or weeks, then get hammered by a new offensive. My response was to retreat to the new normal level of physical and cognitive functioning.

During my first few years of grace with Parkinson's, I coined the term "less-ability" in contradistinction to "disability." People loved the panache and glass-half-full attitude. I was a 45-year-old poster boy for that positive, young-onset "I can still do all this stuff I've always done" Parkinson's patient.

I've actually had Parkinson's for one-third of my life. I'm now 60. The adaptive yoga class I've been in for the past 10 years has become more difficult to keep up with. When our teacher recently said that we were working at just about the level of her "normal" classes, and that we were much stronger now, it made me feel better. But not much. I don't feel stronger. A decade ago, I was still okay with the "new normal" paradigm, because I could live and function with the level of change. There were still moments when I wasn't aware I had Parkinson's symptoms.

But when the new normal started to encroach on my identity, I saw the insidious nature of constant retrenchment. I would have to give up some very important parts of my life. The disease had finally gotten down to the bone.

I still have good "on" times, though shorter now, but have found the need to make lifestyle changes, such as being matched up with an assistance dog to help me break freezing episodes and help me keep my balance when I'm walking. Finn was to be my "balance dog" in more than one sense. He was going to help me stay more emotionally balanced. I get discouraged that I literally have to relearn how to walk every morning. Finn could have helped out here, too, by stepping lightly on my foot to break the "freeze" I experience as the inability to make my feet move once I am standing up. (Read more about my experience with Finn in Chapter 19, "The Tortoise Dances.")

Some changes, new normals, take years to play out. Two things I've always identified myself with are bicycling and guitar playing. It was 20 years ago that I felt the twinges of compromised articulation in the fingers of my right, my picking, hand. But no one else noticed. It has progressed to the stage where people notice. It's obvious. I've announced several times in the last ten years that I can "no longer play the guitar." I had been an accomplished finger-picker and flat-picker, playing since my teens. But I keep a guitar, a nice little 1930 concert-style Stella, and still play it from time to time. I believe that such core activities should not be abandoned lightly, regardless of what I've said to other people. I keep trying. I adjust my standards. I simplify.

Same with bicycling, although for safety reasons and increasing car traffic, I have actually ceased to ride—that decision was a years-long process as well. This has created awkward moments, such as when I browse in local bike shops where the employees know me, and someone says, "I thought you stopped riding." Well, today I might be able to ride, or to play guitar. I'm not sure how to respond. I try not to take on the responsibility for being consistent about my abilities from day to day.

So, again, who am I? Here's what I believe. I am a collection of selves (not "personalities") that are unique entities, and those self-identifying entities are held in active tension by something greater than the sum of the parts. I believe I am holding the fragment selves (the bicycle rider, the guitarist, the functioning lover, the kitchen general, the writer, the dancer, etc.) within the unity of my higher, or deeper, meaning as a person.

Buckminster Fuller got it right when he said, "I seem to be a verb." There is a dynamic quality to life, with or without Parkinson's disease. Parkinson's just forces the question of identity at least to be asked.

Seeing the layers of ability-dependent identity peeled back, onion-like, as a result of having the disease has made me aware that I am more than what is revealed in those layers. This is the gift of Parkinson's disease, as well as probably any chronic illness: to make us look for meaning beyond "what I can do," so that the answer to the question "Who am I?" becomes, "I just am." That's what I need to practice.

It sounds simple, but it's not a static state. My various selves may come and go as I identify with one or more of them for a period of time. This becomes a spiritual endeavor, if you want to think about it in those terms. It is really a search for meaning in my life.

In the future, when someone asks me "How are you?" I'll acknowledge that I appreciate their asking, and probably say, "Pretty good today." They are not asking about my existential status, and a smarty-alecky reply would be inappropriate. I am just exploring what goes through my mind as I contemplate these everyday social interactions and the way they can lead to deeper issues.

Parkinson's is wearing me out. But I have inspiring role models in my support group, as well as a couple of inspiring folks outside the group, who are facing more advanced-stage symptoms and disability, and doing so with grace, a sense of humor, and a deep commitment to staying alive and vital. I think I have a clearer picture of who they are than I would if we didn't share this peculiar affliction.

3.

I Get By with a Little Help from My Friends

Last April I went out on a limb in an e-mail to a group of my male friends. These are guys I know from playing music and through our once-a-month "philosophy on tap" gatherings. We meet to have a pint or two and try to solve the world's problems. I know; we're not doing a very good job.

Although I'm about a decade older than most of these guys, we have several common interests and we all know a little about one another. For example, they all know I have Parkinson's disease, which I was diagnosed with in 1998, but until recently most didn't really know exactly what Parkinson's entails for me.

My e-mail started out: "Hi guys. My life is kind of messed up right now." I went on to ask for their help.

It had been a pretty rough patch for me. I'd been experiencing bouts of depression and was concerned because my wife and caregiver, Lee, had two out-of-town trips scheduled. These trips meant I'd be by myself for about two weeks out of a two-month period. Instead of gritting my teeth and telling Lee I'd be fine, I acknowledged my concerns and reached out. I told my friends I needed help with meals during my wife's absence because I tend not to eat well, or much at all, when she's away. (I'm already underweight and can't afford to lose more.)

I'm also susceptible to feelings of isolation, and I wanted to make sure I'd have companionship for evening meals.

I told my friends I couldn't manage to organize a schedule and asked them to do what they could. The response surprised me—and not just my friends' overwhelming desire to help. I was also bowled over when I learned that a group of men can create the kind of support structure women are so good at in times of need.

One of the guys set up a schedule and shared it with the group. Others filled it in, committing to a meal or two.

It turned out to be enlivening and enlightening. Over dinner, and sometimes beers, I got to know a couple of the men I hadn't really known well prior to our "food support circle."

Two or three of my support-team members told me they really admired me for asking for help, something they said would have been hard for them to do.

It amazed me how, in one of my darker hours, I had inadvertently touched something in these men: a desire to help. And in helping, they told me, they found a level of joy. This certainly runs contrary to the view of men not being nurturers.

How was the food, you may ask? It was great. And while the food was important, what I remember most about these two weeks is the enjoyment of spending time individually with my friends, each of them busy raising kids, working, and trying to carve out time for themselves, but then making the time to bring me dinner.

One effort I especially admired was Matt's variation on a chef's salad. It was delivered in an aluminum lasagna pan. "I hope it's okay," Matt said. "I've never made a salad before." Matt, a soft-spoken teacher, was really working outside his comfort zone. The salad was delicious.

Another evening I was picked up by Chris, who drove me across town to have dinner with his family, including his wife, two sons, and his wife's parents. It was a joy and a privilege to spend time with these lovely folks. As Chris was driving me home, we agreed it had been a wonderful night.

Dan, in the midst of a job change, was having difficulty keeping up with the daily demands on his time and energy and forgot to sign up for a meal. He called me after my wife returned, feeling bad about not helping out. I told him not to feel bad, that I was just glad he'd called.

The next evening Dan and I went out for pizza and conversation, touching on some of the issues that run deep for men but that mainly go untalked about. I feel this episode strengthened our friendship.

These guys are all great, and I am thankful that Dan, Paul, Don, Chris, Rodd, and Matt are men I can call friends. It was "only" dinner and a bit of conversation, but it made an enormously positive impact on my outlook while I was alone.

Maybe at the next "philosophy on tap" meeting at one of our several favorite local pubs, we will actually solve one of the world's problems as we linger over pints of microbrew. In a sense, maybe we did begin to solve one of those problems: the idea that men don't have the capacity to care for one another.

For now, though, I just want to say, "Thanks, guys! I love you!"

4.

"Dad, Am I Going to Start Shaking?"

The first time my son Eli, now 26, asked a question about Parkinson's disease he was in the sixth grade. He walked into the bedroom, where my wife and I sleep, and where I had been taking an afternoon rest. I sat up as he plunked down on the edge of the bed.

"Dad," he said, the tone of his voice making him sound much older than he was. "Am I going to start shaking, like you?"

What a good and obvious question—yet one that never occurred to me as something a 12-year-old would ask. I considered how I should reply, feeling that he wanted more definitive information than being told, "It's not likely you'll ever start shaking." So I said, "No, you're not going to start shaking. I'm sorry if you've been worrying about that. But I'm glad you asked."

He tugged at a loose thread on the blanket and said, "Dad, can we go play some catch?"

I replied that we sure could, and we got up from the bed to go find the baseball and our gloves. Everything seemed, for the time being, a lot better.

But I didn't really know for a fact that he would never have PD. There is evidence coming out of Parkinson's studies that seems to suggest the somewhat ambiguous conclusion that genetic factors combined with exposure to environmental toxins are probably involved in developing some form of parkinsonism. Which does not really say whether the genetic connection is a key element. If Eli were to ask me today whether he would get Parkinson's, I would have to say, "I really just don't know."

When Eli asked his question, he was looking for reassurance. At that point, I was able to give it to him. It was the right thing to do, then.

The question whether to tell the whole truth is a tough call. It came up, in a different form, years earlier, before I had Parkinson's disease.

Eli was nine years old and had been asking for a dog, so Lee and I decided it was time for a family pooch. It was a Christmas surprise for our son. The dog Lee and I chose at the Humane Society shelter wasn't a puppy, but she was still young at 6 months. Lee wanted to name the dog Zola, and so it was.

Zola seemed docile at first, which we liked. We found out later that before releasing a dog for adoption, the dog gets a round of antibiotics to take care of "kennel cough" or whatever they might have picked up from other dogs at the shelter.

It takes a few days for the antibiotic to get the dog back to his or her normal behavior. After having her in our house for two or three days, Zola became a different dog. Her energy was very high. Her temperament seemed fine when she was with people, but she began showing signs of dog-aggression, especially with dogs on leashes. We went to obedience-training classes, had in-home sessions with the local dog whisperer, and asked the shelter if they could give us any help.

Once dogs find some way to get what they want, they'll

use that behavior again and again. Zola learned that she could just leap over the gate to get out of our yard, so we had a new six-foot gate built and installed. On the day that was to be her last, she saw or smelled or heard a dog playing with children down on the next block. I watched in amazement and horror as Zola literally climbed over the gate. That was it. She went into attack mode, zeroing in on the other dog. Pretty soon neighbors and children were screaming and I was running and the neighbor's dog was down, but fortunately not badly injured.

The dog shamans we contacted said this behavior would only get worse. Lee and I were told that our only choice was to have Zola put down. The Humane Society people said they could not place her again with the problems that had emerged so dramatically.

We agreed to tell Eli that Zola had gone away to live on a farm in eastern Washington, where there were no dogs on leashes and where there was room for her to run. That Zola just couldn't live with us in the city.

In his twenties, Eli actually said that telling him the truth about Zola at the time would probably have been hard for him to deal with. So maybe we guessed right.

In 2003, on a warm fall day in Missoula, Montana, Lee and I were visiting Eli at the beginning of his third year at the University of Montana. He had rented a house on Rattlesnake Drive with two friends, and was in the process of expressing his anger about the fact that we, his mother and father, had wasted the money he could have used for college, squandering it instead on tuition at a K-through-8 Waldorf school in Bellingham.

I was having a hard time. My DBS settings (see Glossary) were just not right. I carried a remote with which

I could turn the stimulation on and off. When it was on, I was getting depressed and weepy. If it was off, dyskinesias and primary symptoms started to emerge. It was driving me crazy.

I don't remember if the damn thing was on or off, but I was withering under Eli's offensive. I had to go outside and sit on a rock, sobbing, feeling like the lousiest parent on earth. It was all my fault!

Lee and Eli came outside a few minutes later. I was sensitive about being seen like that. Lee asked me what was wrong. "I'm a shitty father," I said, hanging my head.

"Dad, no way," Eli said and gave me a hug (amazing, as he is not generous with us in that way). "I remember whenever I was down when I was a kid, you'd take me out to play catch. How many other dads would just go out and do that?"

Any dad worth his salt, I said to myself, feeling a little better.

I thought about the day he'd asked me if he was going to "start shaking" like his dad, and about the clear, reassuring answer I'd given him—something I know now I can't guarantee, if anything in life can be guaranteed.

But the afternoon in Montana is a sweet memory. Dad, the tortoise, being comforted by his nearly grown son, the hare who made his way through college on a track scholarship, whose main concern was running fast.

"You're a great dad," he said as I wiped tears from my cheek.

5.

Married but Not Dead

I didn't really understand what it is like to have a chronic illness until I had one. I tried to empathize with and be supportive of my wife Lee after her diagnosis of rheumatoid arthritis (RA) in 1986. The life-changing symptoms began in earnest a few weeks after our son was born. But I didn't really "get" it. I wasn't yet living with PD.

Major life-defining transitions—giving birth to a first child, hearing the feared diagnosis, losing a parent, or worse, losing one's child—are perhaps only vaguely imaginable to someone who hasn't yet experienced the transition. Until that birth or loss or fundamental life change has happened to a person, it is beyond the range of one's direct experience, and it is impossible, really, to know how life changes and perspective shifts.

I was impatient and judgmental with Lee in the early years of her RA. Both of us drifted into depression that made life extremely difficult, especially with a young son to raise. I went to work in the morning and got things done. Lee, however, had little to show for herself at the end of the day. Keeping Eli clean, fed, and entertained was just about all she could manage. I discovered that I was angry, but it felt wrong to direct it outwards, so I bottled it up.

After I'd struggled with Parkinson's for a while, I reacted to Lee's problems differently. It may sound trite, but once

I was diagnosed with PD, I had compassion for my wife; I understood. It wasn't that she wanted to move slowly and fearfully, or to be crabby, exhausted, and depressed from dealing with significant pain and fatigue every day. Now we were on the same side of the fence that divides the world of health and the world of illness.

The fence dividing those worlds is real, although it can't be seen. You know when you have crossed it, because it's almost like a separate language is spoken and different social mores are now in place.

But once you've learned the new language, you can barely remember the one spoken in the world you left behind. One can hardly recall how to "act" in order to be seen as acceptably normal.

If chronic illness is a foreign land, well, there you are. Everyday things sound, smell, and look different than what you may be used to experiencing. You wonder: What's next?

I didn't realize initially that I needed to make peace with my new condition and situation. But it's likely to be a fairly rough ride through life without some agreement about the rules of engagement. Both acceptance and positive denial might serve as starting points. In the meantime, I try being kinder to myself. My cat knows when I need a break. She hops up on the desk and walks across the computer keyboard to get my attention. "Oh," I tell her, "you want me to stop what I'm doing and go lie down on the sofa so that you can be admired and petted."

I used to just ignore her when she walked right in front of the screen, but now I've learned to pay attention to what she says.

Both Lee and I carried baggage from our lives before we met. She'd been married twice, both marriages ending in divorce. I had been in two significant relationships but abandoned the first one and was abandoned in the second. Formative experiences with our parents, the skeletons in the dark closet of family secrets, our cultural beliefs, our sexuality—all these and more we hauled along into our marriage and our life together.

Both of us have talked about feeling unlovable, to each other as well as in general, a belief that causes so much pain and is so pervasive and entrenched that it takes an enormous effort to counteract—far more effort than attending a three-day retreat led by a marriage counselor, or reading a book on relationships. Just to regain and retain a more loving self-image can be a real challenge.

Not that there's anything wrong with weekend retreats and books about relationships. I am not suggesting that we didn't need that sort of help. We needed, and still need, a ton of help from medical providers, counselors, psychiatrists, healers, friends, groups, support networks, insurance companies, Wall Street, the U.S. Government, technology, tai-chi, qigong, yoga, and dance. I'm sure we also get help we're not even aware of. I think I speak for both of us when I say that we are grateful for all our blessings, even, in a way, including the realignment of who we are on the chronic-illness side of the fence.

What about sex and disability? That is, of course, delicate territory, and there is no easy path. Sex becomes that much more complicated with the overlay of chronic illness. Sexual intimacy, among both the well and the ill, brings its own prickly thorns: desire, jealousy, disappointment, pain, ecstasy, loss of libido, hypersexuality, physical limitations, even violence and abuse, on the darkest end of the spectrum. To be honest, I don't think that describing that part of our relationship would be therapeutic for Lee or for me, and I feel extremely uncomfortable saying even that much. A sexual relationship for those with chronic illness of any kind requires flexibility and innovation. But, for anyone, physical limitations and drug side-effects, as well as coexisting conditions such as depression, can turn love-making into a difficult and frustrating experience. This can be due to both disease progression and the side-effects of Parkinson's medications on one's libido. It isn't hard for me to understand why this aspect of PD treatment isn't widely discussed.

Lee and I have been married nearly 30 years, parts of it wonderful, parts of it not so wonderful. But I keep coming back to this idea of forgotten love. We have to remind ourselves that it takes work and an open heart to recall that which has been forgotten and neglected. We are one another's caregiver. Mostly, these days, Lee is more on the "giver" side of our relationship, but we both know that could change in a minute. Our situation is not unique. The fact that we can both relate to having a chronic illness might work in our favor as a couple. I have seen and heard very sad stories of marriages that don't survive when only one of the couple becomes chronically ill, and the partner can't deal with that fact because he or she can't relate.

Beyond the diagnosis of Parkinson's disease, or rheumatoid arthritis, there is a whole life to live. Lee and I have found sometimes converging, sometimes parallel, sometimes diverging pathways to follow in our lives as individuals. There is no denying that our activities have been reduced in scope and intensity, some even jettisoned altogether, and yet we seem to be living useful lives, together as well as separately. We encourage and help each other to remember what is important.

6.

Tess of the d'Urbervilles, Uncle Larry, and Me

I earnestly read Thomas Hardy's novel *Tess of the d'Urbervilles* in college in 1972. I've more recently watched film director Roman Polanski's adaptation to the movie screen, titled simply *Tess*, starring the stunningly beautiful, porcelain-skinned Natasha Kinski. Whether one reads the original Hardy or sees Polanski's filmic adaptation, it is a powerful love story and a heartbreaking tragedy.

Would I have the patience and concentration to read the Hardy novel today? I'm not sure. Parkinson's disease and the medications I take to reduce symptoms are at least partly responsible for my current difficulties in reading anything too complex or lengthy. I can't blame everything on PD, but I am sure there has been an impact on my cognitive abilities.

One line that Tess utters at a low point in her barely-more-than-a-child life, still resonates: "All is vanity," she whispers to herself upon awakening, out alone in the woods, unable to go home, unwilling to be pulled into the orbit of Alec d'Urberville, a non-blood relation from a family who had "bought" the name of the once-aristocratic family line from which Tess was descended.

Drawn from the Book of Ecclesiastes, the phrase sug-

gests the futility of human effort, as well as the emptiness of the world. For Tess, life's shiny surface, including
her physical beauty, actually become random attributes,
beneath which lurk wounded souls, worm-eaten remains
of our once-living flesh, and an overwhelming sense of
nothingness. Kinski's Tess is a tragic protagonist in an
extended existential crisis.

Although I don't believe I do well with chronic angst, I
have experienced times when all seemed futile. I don't know
where this journey with Parkinson's disease is taking me,
but as I travel the road—both believing and not believing
in the goodness of the world, seeing and not seeing the suffering experienced by myself as well as others, feeling and
not feeling the joy of being alive—my "self" gets smaller
and smaller, taking up less space and becoming less likely
to indulge in distractions such as regret, self-pity, and
blame.

Later in the Hardy novel, Tess peers through an iron
grille and into the blackness of the crypt where the remains
of her once wealthy d'Urberville ancestors are entombed.
"Why am I on the wrong side of this door?" she says.

Clearly, the young woman is depressed, a state that
may have responded to talk therapy and antidepressant
medications, had they been available.

Parkinson's disease wasn't even identified as a distinct
illness until 1817, with the publication of James Parkinson's
"Essay on the Shaking Palsy," and it took until the 1960s
for levodopa and carbidopa to be widely used in combination as a treatment that helps ease the major motor symptoms of Parkinson's disease.

My uncle on my dad's side, Dad's brother-in-law Larry,

had Parkinson's in the late 1950s, almost a century and a half after Dr. Parkinson's essay was written. Uncle Larry sat in a wheelchair, his face expressionless, unable to move, or even talk. Modern medicine didn't have much to offer him.

Before I was diagnosed with PD, I tended to hypochondriacal lunacy, seeing the most benign changes in my body or experiencing unusual sensations as a sure sign that I had a terrible disease and would be dead ere the next fortnight arrived. I, however, had an advantage over Tess in self-diagnosis and ultimately self-care. I had the Internet. I was able to pretty much diagnose myself with PD.

Actually, I was initially diagnosed with parkinsonism, a more general term that includes idiopathic Parkinson's disease as well as a number of atypical manifestations, none of which anyone would want (e.g., progressive supranuclear palsy and multiple-system atrophy). Atypical parkinsonism comes with a bleak prognosis.

Had Tess d'Urberville been in a position to google terms such as *depression, patriarchy, late 18th-century women's rights in England*, and perhaps *oppression*, she may have been able to find resources for change rather than capitulate to the rules of the game that staunchly defended the status quo.

I felt great relief when my neurologist, Dr. Patrick Delaney, gave me an official diagnosis of Parkinson's disease. I don't think most people have this reaction, but I had learned enough about the disease to know it isn't fatal; that is, people can die of conditions or complications brought on by PD, but they don't actually die of Parkinson's disease itself.

Somehow, this isn't as reassuring as it used to be. But

at the time, by proactively ferreting out all the information I could gather on Parkinson's, I discovered that there were tools available that could keep me going for many years: medications, surgical intervention (deep-brain stimulation), movement disorder specialists, physical and occupational therapists, speech pathologists, neuro-psychologists … the list goes on. I live in a much better time than Uncle Larry lived for someone who has Parkinson's disease. A wheelchair was about the only tool at his disposal. I would say, in spite of what I have just written, that Uncle Larry died of Parkinson's disease. The specific condition that causes death isn't the salient fact. In the post mortem, all is vanity.

After Tess murders the sinister Alec d'Urberville, an act that is both redemptive and a death sentence, she whispers to her prodigal husband, the conflicted Angel Clare, "They'll hang me, won't they, Angel?"

Oh, how I wish Tess had seen and realized a better end for herself—something other than becoming a hunted criminal—but in fact there was really no out for her in that cultural and historical context. Women worked like dogs. Fortunes were married to fortunes to create even more wealth, primarily for men. Women had no voice, no power. Struggling alone against those impediments took too much of Tess. Her death wish was ultimately granted.

As I consider Uncle Larry, his limited therapeutic options, and Tess's need for a good psychiatrist, with whom she had no chance of getting an appointment before next March, maybe things aren't as grim for me as I sometimes think. Cure for Parkinson's? Maybe someday. For now, I've got my DBS goin'; I've got my colorful and potent tablets and capsules. I see a psychiatrist every couple of months and travel the 90 miles from Bellingham to visit my neurologist in Seattle when I need to. There is still evidence of life in this 60-year-old mind and body. So maybe things aren't so dire after all.

Tess was indeed hanged for her crime.

But I think tomorrow will be a good day.

7.

Being Amazing

I want to spend a little time saying what I can about some of the most amazing people I've never met. There are some extraordinary humans out there whom I have met, and I'll talk about them, too.

First, about me. More than halfway through the calendar year on my journey to my sixty-something birthday, it is becoming clear to me that it takes more energy than I can muster to be an amazing person. But I know that amazing people in the world, including people with Parkinson's disease (PWPs) might be able to show us something about being courageous in the face of adversity.

At some point following a Parkinson's diagnosis, PWPs make decisions that help them deal with the uninvited guest at the party. There are people who need to fight back. They decide, for example, that at least attempting to climb Mt. Everest makes sense and feels like the right thing to do. Or he or she may decide on a cross-country bicycle trip to spread awareness of Parkinson's disease. Or perhaps a PWP gets a chance to raft through the Grand Canyon on the Colorado River. Maybe she or he will take a skydiving lesson, or anything that makes one feel alive and that might inspire other PWPs to fight back at whatever parts of our brains and bodies have betrayed us.

I have not been such an amazing person. Sometimes

I feel more like an old gossip, for instance, when I talk to other people with Parkinson's about our medications and doses, when our first symptoms appeared, why somebody stopped coming to support group meetings. Shop talk, really. It's as though I am positioning myself to be seen as somebody who is deeply into the Parkinson's-related "stuff" that accumulates like dust in a corner.

I have been saying recently that I've had Parkinson's for one-third of my life. The statement reflects a certain amount of bravado and pride. It's essentially true, but so what?

Since my diagnosis in 1998, I have rarely wondered "why" I have "it," or what it "means" to live with Parkinson's disease.

Nor do I spend much time publicly addressing my sense of mortality, as I was asked to do in a recent interview. "I might get hit by a truck tomorrow" is all I can say about the fruitless nature of prophecy. Even with a sense of fatalism, chances are I will wake up tomorrow, still have Parkinson's disease, and not get hit by a truck. I'm not saying don't make practical end-of-life decisions while you are still able to do so. But death is not the problem. Life, if anything, is the problem; it's messy, confusing, painful, as well as joyous and deeply meaningful. Amazing people, perhaps, experience a more immediate awareness of the need to fight entropy and be closer to the sources of life and death, to live as if one's life depended on it.

Envision a late-stage Parkinson's death? I'll pass on that.

I do know PWPs who show their amazingness more quietly: people like Diane, an elderly woman who on some days can barely move. And yet she still comes to our Parkinson's dance class, helped by a wonderful caregiver. Even though Diane can't move much or even express herself verbally, she participates in a meaningful way. Meaningful for her as well as for the other members of the class. When something is funny and she smiles, that is amazing.

Consider my friend Mike, who has lived with Parkinson's for nearly three decades and yet attends a yoga class twice a week, sometimes rolling into the church parking lot in one of his restored early 1950s cars, in which the driver sits on the right, British style. Given PWPs' difficulties with left-right crossbrain function, I am impressed that Mike can move back and forth between driving on the right and on the left.

I didn't know Mike before he had Parkinson's disease. We talk about the disease and both know how it chips away at our foundations, until finally we fall—literally as well as in the sense of surrendering territory in our essential selves, our individual identities. Although he doesn't "do" much art any longer, Mike is a a clay artist, a sculptor, a creative person with a body that makes creativity problematic at best.

For me, there is no doubt that Mike is an amazing person.

Facing illness or bad news of any kind, we all respond in different ways. Karen, in my support group, has shared her rationale for not "fighting" Parkinson's. I tend to agree. In a pitched battle, Parkinson's will ultimately win. By not rising to the bait and becoming "warriors" in the battle, we fight in a different way—for recognition, awareness, and respect as human beings. I hang onto what I can do until it is clear to me that a belief, activity, or goal is no longer relevant to my personal journey and growth.

Amazing people are heroic, either publicly or in the less-visible background of life. Trying to climb Mt. Everest doesn't strike me personally as a good idea. And, to be serious, I am not sure any person with Parkinson's disease has ever made the attempt. A group of PWPs with the help of a wilderness outfitter climbed Mt. Kilimanjaro recently. It seemed like it was a very difficult trip, and in fact a few members of the climbing party said they were still recovering months later. But as I looked at the photos and heard the stories of the trip, my primary reaction was envy.

The impulse to be amazing connects the heroic defense of our aliveness to whatever shape or form our courage may take. The common denominator is our mortality and the voice within that whispers, conspiratorially, "Be amazing."

8.

Why Don't You Talk about Me?

When I was out walking the neighborhood in the melancholy late November gloom, I saw a light on in our neighbors' townhouse. I knew that they had just paid a contractor to install two flights of powered chair-lifts in their unit. My wife and I had been interested in such a system in our two-story unit so that we could continue to live here if one of us—me, most likely—became unable to negotiate stairs. So I rang the doorbell.

"Try it out," Phil encouraged me. I put the seat and the foot rest in place, sat down and pushed a button. It made an electrical hum as the motor pulled me up to the landing.

During that 15-second trip, I felt like I had aged 10 years, as if I'd been thrust forward in a time machine. It was the same feeling I had when Lee and I tried out a Parkinson's support group at a local retirement manor at which the group members were mostly older and in advanced stages of the disease. I had strong conviction that this is not where I'm going to go, for as long as I can avoid it. The experience made me fearful of becoming "them," the "others."

I left the the neighbors' home after getting out of the chair lift and expressing my genuine gratitude for letting me interrupt whatever they had been doing. They're very sweet people, and I learned something: I was afraid not only of getting old and infirm, but of depending too much on gadgets and unaffordable lifestyle adjustments just to maintain a semblance of independence, of being functional alone.

But what do I know about what other people think and feel that makes life worth hanging on to? Nothing. I impose my selective filter on every emotion, opinion, and reaction that I experience.

A real tortoise would not have this problem. A tortoise is protected by a hard shell. His existence is binary—either he's in or he's out. No reflection, no second-guessing, no wondering what other tortoises think or say about him.

As a person with Parkinson's disease, I care in a few different ways what people think about me. First, I get useful feedback from people I see on a periodic basis. A fellow yoga student might say, after being gone for a month, "You look really good," even though I don't remember her saying "You look really awful" at some earlier time. But it's still good to hear.

In general, when people tell me I look "good," they are being incredibly thoughtful and trying to help. But all I can think is, why do I look so good if I'm feeling so crummy?

After DBS surgery and subsequent programming, I initially felt that I hadn't gained much ground. I was unable to reduce my medication and have longer "on" times, which was my hope and expectation. But my friends told me that my body was a lot more "quiet." And it occurred to me that my dyskinesias were far less severe, were in fact almost gone. I had been looking at the glass half-empty, ignoring the real progress I had made.

The second reason I care what people think of me is not just peculiar to PWPs: I need validation. As I try learning modern dance, I receive encouragement, help, and opportunities to shine.

As the author of a recently published collection of short stories, I was amazed to find the room full when I gave a reading at our local independent bookstore. People I know, as well as a few strangers, bought the book. Validation Central. When I entered some poems in competitions, my poems were selected to be read at workshops and performances. I even tried modeling for a human-figure painting class. It was harder than I thought it would be. All in all, I'm good in the validation department.

The third reason I care about what people think of me is that at least they're thinking about me. I have not disappeared, not turned my head to the wall in despair and defeat like Burt Lancaster in the screen version of Ernest Hemingway's story "The Killers."

I'm not asking "Do you love me?" or "Am I a good/bad person?" Simply knowing more about how I look and behave from a not-me point of view can give useful information about possible disease progression, the impact of different interventions (e.g., DBS surgery), my apparent cognitive state, and my mood. Despite my guarded attitude about being told I am looking good, that is really my favorite comment, and I can't take it as anything less than a self-worth-reinforcing compliment.

In fact, none of this feedback is trivial to me as I try to hold myself together, as piece by piece the person I once thought I was no longer appears the same—as I am slowly deconstructed. I think differently than I used to think, and I can't figure out exactly what it is, but I feel as though I am thinking smaller (the topic of the next chapter); my ability to stand back and take a less myopic account of myself has diminished. It is an uneasy feeling, like something is missing.

Having said that, I'm still here today, trying to live a life that except for the occasional late-November, early-evening swoon seems to be pretty good. I'm grateful for it.

I'm going to stay off the chair-lift to the second floor, however, at least for now.

9.

Smaller Than Life

Some days I look out and just can't see the rich fabric of life. It's like I am unable to filter anything, the good or the bad. Life begins to feel random; people start to seem unfriendly. Yuck! I'm depressed again.

Often, the world that makes sense to me is right before my eyes, multihued and wonderfully complex. I, however, may be too depressed to raise my head and look.

Depression and Parkinson's disease, both neurological illnesses, are familiar bedfellows. I believe depression arguably can result from the awareness of having PD, a chronic, incurable, progressive brain disease of unknown origin. But not everybody with Parkinson's becomes depressed. And not everyone who is depressed begins at some point to show symptoms of PD. Yet if I am not misinformed, the current thinking is that depression can be an early symptom of Parkinson's disease.

In my early twenties I felt that something was changing inside me. I go back to my personal journals from that period in my life and find writing that looks and reads as if it had been *thrown* down onto the paper. Sometimes, mid-sentence, the writing stops, maybe starting later on a different, randomly selected page. I was depressed. Part of my brain was broken, the damage seemingly reflected in the discontinuity of my prose.

I didn't really have a name for this state of suffering in a meaningless world. I didn't think of myself as "depressed." Life was just hard.

Finally, thankfully, my wife told me, many years later, that "it" was getting worse and that I'd better do something about it.

About a year before my Parkinson's diagnosis, I finally agreed to try an antidepressant, and it worked. I am convinced that this saved not only my marriage but also my life. Helping my brain to heal was perhaps the reason I received my PD diagnosis with such equanimity.

I still have depressive episodes, but they are much shorter, and the characteristic "feel" of the depression has changed. Whereas before antidepressants, the root emotion was anger, depressive episodes now have more a quality of sadness.

I would characterize depression as a condition in which I feel smaller than life. My mind sees only limitations, insufficiencies, and withdrawal. In a parallel way, Parkinson's disease is the physical expression of the depressive state, as we lose our abilities to communicate, express feelings, and move our bodies.

An elderly friend told me she had gone to see her doctor to have him look at some red welt-like spots on her arm. She feared the worst: some aggressive form of skin cancer, or a life-threatening MRSA infection, perhaps.

The doctor looked closely at the area she was concerned about, shook his head, and told her with a straight face, "Don't worry. It's just the evil trying to get out."

He was jesting, of course, as his patient well knew. But it actually seems not so far-fetched. Shamans in aboriginal cultures still perform exorcisms to remove evil energy from their clients' bodies. Is the doctor's joke any less compelling or useful than if he had said, "The raised red skin suggests an inflammatory process. I'm not sure what's causing it, but let's give it a week and we'll take another look."

Is depression the evil trying to get out? Maybe not, maybe so.

I have to confess something. I have been, until recently (really!), afraid of the dark. As my Parkinson's has progressed, however, this fear that something awful may happen to me has mainly been fear of something dreadful out there that is going to get me. But the source of my fear is not the monsters and murderers I can imagine waiting for me in the darkened bedroom.

The real monster is my own condition. It's not some limpid vampire lying in wait in the closet. It is falling down on my way to the bathroom in the middle of the night, in the dark. The evil is being unable to take a step forward. It is the shaking and dyskinesia, it is the fatigue, it is the loss of my libido, it is my periodic incontinence, it is going insane when I take too much dopamine agonist.

How does this new (for me) paradigm of illness—or evil, if you will—affect the depression that can come with Parkinson's disease? I don't know. I will say that for a decade, in my late thirties and early forties, I was afraid of taking antidepressant medication, as recommended by my doctor. My fear was that I would become something that was not-me. After years of frustration with alternative ways of treating my mood disorder, what finally changed my thinking was a brochure that contained informative results from a recent clinical report on depression. I'd done lots of reading about depression, but this report was the first time I'd seen the words *brain, depression,* and *healing* used in the same sentence. "Healing" isn't in the main-stream medical lexicon. But it is a word that I can relate to in a stronger way than I can relate to neurological and psychiatric jargon.

My paradigm change allowed me to understand that antidepressant drug therapy was a means to give my brain a chance to heal. My brain is a good one. It was just broken and needed a little help to rediscover its balance. Looking at my reluctance to medicate for depression to that point, I saw that I just needed to refocus the lens I was looking through. No other factors had changed—only my perception and belief.

Now my brain is broken in some different ways, and the combination of medications that I take and the DBS programming I receive are all working on a fairly small piece of my cerebral real estate. I could make the case that the "I" whom everybody sees is really just a hodgepodge of chemical and electrical interactions that sometimes make me wonder who I am besides the product of all those adjustments. But that line of reasoning is somewhat depressing in itself.

Soren Kierkegaard, the Danish theologian writing during the 19th century, advises, "Be that self which one truly is."

If only that were as simple as it sounds. Depression creates confusion and mayhem that exhausts me. Depression reinforces the buttresses of the castle to make the walls stronger and higher. Inside the castle is what my shadow self is protecting: the great secret. The answer to the question, "Who am I?"

10.

The Dog and Tortoise Show

Not long before I stopped working for a living in 2002, I was sitting at home in front of the computer, wistfully browsing PetFinder, looking at dogs who needed homes. We'd lost our dog recently, and hadn't considered getting another so soon.

Then I saw, listed in the "senior" category, a photo of a dog named Barney, who at that time was fostered out through a wonderful dog rescue agency in Mill Creek, just north of Seattle. A shepherd mix with the kindest face on earth, one ear floppy and the other standing at attention, Barney was probably 13 years old when we adopted him. It was understood that this would likely be his last stop, his "forever home."

We enjoyed and took care of him for four good years, during which time he captured many hearts, until finally, at somewhere between 17 and 18 years of age, Barney became unable to stand or control his bladder or bowels. Sadly, we made the decision to put him down. I'll never forget his last look into my eyes when we said goodbye. I'm not sure whether he was asking for permission to go, or saying, "It's okay, I'm tired. I'm ready."

I've been a dog person without a dog ever since.

But a couple years ago, as Parkinson's was biting at my heels like a tireless puppy, I found a service-dog training organization in Anacortes, Washington, a town steeped in commercial fishing history, a place not located on or near any interstate highway, boasting a thriving downtown and Main Street, and, looking west, sporting beautiful views of the San Juan Islands.

The organization, Summit Assistance Dogs, is a not-for-profit enterprise whose goal is to provide professionally trained service dogs to qualified disabled applicants, regardless of their ability to pay. The usual wait time for being matched with a canine partner is two to five years, with no guarantee that you will *ever* be paired up.

It was difficult to imagine in what kind of condition I might be five years hence. But I submitted my application in 2009 and hoped for the best—not having a clear idea what "the best" would look like.

Requesting a dog to help me with balance and gait freezing, to get me outside walking more, and to provide companionship, as I tend to isolate myself socially, seemed like a good idea. I would be getting something "new." I'm ashamed to admit that it felt a bit like I was anticipating the arrival of a new high-end bicycle, but not knowing if or when it would arrive.

Even Summit's well-trained dogs are still dogs. They require a lot of attention, they get distracted, they want to play when it's not playtime, they eat, and they excrete bodily waste. They also need washing, grooming, and love, maybe not in that order.

My would-be future partner's name is Finn, short for Finnegan. He was part of a litter sired by a long-haired Collie and whelped by a yellow Lab. The entire litter came out looking like elongated and long-legged black Labs.

In the fall of 2011, I got a call from Erik Mann, an

affable, low-key guy who had been recently hired by Summit to provide outreach and fundraising muscle so that other staff could work on fulfilling the organization's primary goal: training service dogs. Erik asked me if I'd join him on a visit to Naval Station Everett, about 25 miles north of Seattle, where half a dozen ships are home-ported, and to which a few thousand Navy personnel are assigned.

I enthusiastically agreed to go. I'd lived in the Puget Sound region most of my life and had never seen this facility. Erik had to obtain security clearances for us, and then one early-fall morning we set out with two dogs from Summit: the exemplary Phoenix and the irresistible and unschooled Pup-Pup, both Golden Retrievers and crowd pleasers. However, the excitement soon wore Pup-Pup out, and she spent most of the two hours we were there sleeping under the table. The day was sunny but cool, and the exhibitors all set up their tabletop displays outside, enjoying some rare mild fall weather.

We were there as guest exhibitors at a Combined Fund Drive exhibition held in conjunction with a day-long workshop about providing financial support for not-for-profit organizations. Ranking military and civilian personnel on the base participated, and all the exhibitors more or less fit the nonprofit social services profile.

Being on the base that day gave me a new look at American military personnel. Had I assumed they would be essentially different than me? They were interested in what we were doing, came to the table with friends or a spouse, and appeared to face the same problems in life that most of us face each day. Not having enough money, considering having a child, concerned about their health—physical, emotional, and mental.

One couple hung back a few feet from the table. From their conversation, I learned that he had post-traumatic stress syndrome (PTSD). "It's probably too expensive," I overheard him say.

I interrupted to explain that Summit didn't charge anything for their dogs, but clients were encouraged to contribute some amount of money or do volunteer work for the organization, as their particular circumstances allowed. "The only required cost to the applicant is a $25 application fee," I said, hoping I'd gotten that part right. I'm not sure they believed me.

During a lull, I walked over to a grassy playing field where recruits were running, one at a time, around the bases on a field the size of a baseball infield. At each corner, or base, an opponent with padded clothing stood ready to do battle. Each base focused on a different technique: kicking, punching, clobbering the opponent with what looked like a Nerf bat. I don't recall what the guy at home base did, but he looked like he was wearing a bulging Transformer costume. I watched a female recruit run the gauntlet, getting weaker with each combat encounter. I was moved by the verbal support and cheering-on that came from the other recruits, all of them male, waiting their turn. The new coed Navy was having a good morning.

Returning to the Summit table, I found Erik and several conference attendees, so I slipped in and the two of us developed a kind of dog-and-pony show patois. I would talk for a minute about the program, whereupon Erik chimed in with, "Rick has Parkinson's disease, and he's looking forward to finding the right dog to bond with." Then I would explain what it is like to have a disability and be able to tap into this kind of resource. And so on.

After a couple of hours, I began to feel like I was becoming the tortoise again. My body and brain were slowing down, and everything seemed suddenly hard to do. I wanted to pull my head back into my safe dark shell.

As we were beginning to pack up our display materials, most of the Navy people were drifting back into the workshop. Then a seaman of unknown (to me) rank, approached us, walking with some difficulty. He was wearing crisply ironed blue-toned camo pants and shirt, his feet encased in black, shiny combat boots. He looked tired.

I don't even remember his name. I could just tell he was hurting. Neither Erik nor I asked him if he had served in Iraq, or anywhere. But he said he suffered bad PTSD and something was wrong with his legs. He had pain all the time from his waist down.

The soldier smiled briefly at Phoenix and Pup-Pup. I didn't say anything, just listened. He was probably in his late 20s, facing a discharge based on disability. To me, he seemed badly in need of help. The fact that he was just one among thousands of damaged soldiers and vets, many in worse shape than him, didn't decrease my compassion for the soldier or his situation. I felt a connection with another person who was not okay. I didn't say anything about Parkinson's disease. The dogs were getting antsy, too, so we wished the soldier well and got ready to leave.

I watched him as he disappeared into the vanishing point created by the tree-lined walkway that seemed to extend for miles with buildings, all looking the same, lining both sides of the walkway, appearing to become smaller in the distance.

A suddenly colder wind blowing off the water made Erik and me move out to the parking lot quickly, getting the dogs to do their business on a parking strip , then putting dogs and ourselves in the Prius for the trip back to the Mt. Vernon Park-and-Ride lot, where my wife was waiting to take me the rest of the way home.

The dog and tortoise show was over.

ii.

What It's Like

Two dancers and two non-dancing members of the local community walked onto the stage for the first performance of *Stories of Jim and Jo*. Jim Lortz, an actor and Western Washington University faculty member, was diagnosed with Parkinson's disease a few years earlier. Jo Pullen has been struggling with multiple sclerosis (MS) for more than 20 years. It was her initiative that encouraged a collaboration between people with chronic illnesses and the arts community in producing new ways to look at performance as a community process. One outcome was *Stories of Jim and Jo*.

At the beginning of the performance, the dancers asked Jo and Jim questions about what it felt like to have Parkinson's disease or MS. Professional dancer Ian Bivins asked Jim, "Does it look or feel like this?" Whereupon he physically sketched a kinesthetic representation of what PD might feel or look like. I was immediately struck by the accurate freezing gait he performs—the stutter-step, the uncontrolled acceleration of his upper body forward on tiptoe.

"Is it anything like that?"

Jim responded, "Definitely yes, it feels like that!" This line of inquiry continued for a few minutes, and I was both amazed by the accuracy of Ian's improvisation and fascinated by the discrepancy between symptoms that I could understand and those I hadn't experienced. Even though Jim and I have nominally the same disease, how we experience it is very different.

In a sense, I really can't tell you in any comprehensive way what it's like to have Parkinson's disease. A broken toe might be easier to describe (it hurts!). It is hard to keep up with what has changed and continues to change me. I can't compare the variability of symptoms and effects of medication to that of other chronic illnesses, though I imagine there are similarities in the progression of the disease. But does each PWP have a slightly different disease? Or are there different responses to the same disease? And does it matter?

This is the station where I get off the train, because I am not a philosopher of medicine, disease, or the ethics of medical intervention.

I think what matters more than making an academic argument is the fact that variability of response allows us to share and empathize with other PWPs in a more genuine way.

Said another way:

The words *Parkinson's disease* are used to refer to a generalized set of symptoms based on observation and metrics such as the Hoehn and Yahr Scale (see Glossary) that are used to help establish a diagnosis and then periodically grade the severity of symptoms as the disease progresses.

My case is a unique expression of the disease. But while people with Parkinson's talk to neurologists about all the different ways in which the disease manifests in different individuals (some call PD the "boutique" brain disease because of this "customization" of symptoms and intensity), how does anyone know what's really going on for another person? Sometimes not even I know what is going on for me, and I find I need outside input to answer the simple question, "How are you?" Sometimes I'm tempted to ask in return, "Well, how *am* I?"

The generalized profile applied to diagnose a person with Parkinson's yields a clinical best guess based on the process of differential diagnosis. The patient has, or does not have, Parkinson's disease. Or maybe the disease has not yet presented with the cardinal symptoms: bradykinesia, resting tremor, and muscle rigidity. Whatever the case, from inside the experience of being chronically ill, I can't truly understand what Parkinson's is really like for others who have been similarly diagnosed.

Am I alone with "my" Parkinson's disease? Not really. I am able to share my story with other people who are living in their versions of PD, and they can share their stories with me. My disease is unique within a special population (PWPs) that allows communication based both on our commonalities (attributes of the generalized movement disorder frame of reference) and on one's personal narrative describing what it is like for a particular individual to have PD.

That is one reason that my support group is important. A participant can share his or her truth about what he or she is going through. This empowers everyone in the group, because once the unique experience of the individual who has been carrying his or her fear, shame, depression, anger, and who knows what else, has been spoken, the negative emotions are at least partially released and neutralized.

What is it like having Parkinson's disease?

Parkinson's challenges me to maintain a sense of

identity. At times, it is a refuge, such as when I get over-whelmed with trying to be "normal." It is loss of physical abilities and reduced cognitive power. It is a new reality based on a three-hour medication cycle, every day, for the foreseeable future. It is a swift kick in the behind to follow the dictum "use it or lose it" as it applies to both body and mind. It is humbling. It means taking medications that impair my good judgment and cause delusions and para-noia. Like a glacier, it is a slow-moving force that wears me down, grinding me into smaller pieces. And it's a hundred other things, depending on the day.

Parkinson's disease is not a normal (that word again) part of aging. It is not an excuse for giving up your life for PD's sake. "It" doesn't care. PD is not something to be ashamed of. Nor is it something you can carry by yourself. On a practical level at the very least, I need support. I visit a psychologist for counseling when I need help. We don't talk much about Parkinson's disease. Instead, we focus on problem-solving to find a solution to a specific problem or issue I am dealing with.

In the world "out there" I find myself attempting to be a person with Parkinson's disease because I feel some need for a social context, but at the same time I try not to dif-ferentiate just because I have this illness. It is a balancing act. For me, thinking and writing about Parkinson's makes me more aware of what is truly valuable in my life: my wife and son, my ability to continue writing, a caring group of people facing many of the same problems that I have, being a little bit kinder to people, and appreciating every day, even the dark ones.

So does it look or feel anything like this?

I hope that one day the question will become irrelevant, when Dr. Parkinson's "shaking palsy" is a footnote in the dusty archives of medical history.

In the meantime, it's a good question to ask.

12.

The Agonist and the Ecstasy

Youth takes its God-given creativity and talent for granted. At least I did. Now that I possess neither youth nor my former musical ability, I can see what truly precious gifts they were.

For years I've been a folksinger and bluegrass, blues, and Celtic-style guitarist, strumming my first chords when I was 11. As teens, my older brother and I used to play a lot of bluegrass, my brother on the five-string banjo and me on rhythm guitar. I also had an old washboard (I'm not sure where I found one in Long Beach, California) that I played with thimbles on the ends of my fingers, an idea I got from the Nitty-Gritty Dirt Band, who probably got it from Cajun musicians in Louisiana.

To learn the complex, fast-paced bluegrass tunes of Lester Flatt and Earl Scruggs and the Foggy Mountain Boys and the mountain-music breakout group the Dillards, we slowed our record player turntable to 16 $^2/_3$ RPMs from the standard 33 $^1/_3$ RPMs, bringing the tone down an octave and also making the individual notes decipherable. We probably wrecked good Folkways and Vanguard vinyl records, to say nothing of the diamond-tipped needle of our parents' phonograph.

At around the time I was involved in music-making in the early 1970s, something completely unrelated was going on in medical research that would have a profound impact on my life with Parkinson's disease decades later. A new drug class referred to as dopamine agonists (see Glossary) was being studied. One of these was apomorphine, which was beginning to be used as a means to overcome side-effects and loss of levodopa's efficacy in the treatment of Parkinson's disease. However, the agonists come with their own constellation of side-effects, and the difficulty of administration limited its use. Dopamine agonists began to find a place in routine treatment of PD after the discovery of bromocriptine's benefits in PD in 1974, when I was 23 years old.

One of the most difficult things about having Parkinson's disease, which seems as true to me now as it did six or seven years ago, is that it takes away capabilities I've always considered fundamental to my identity.

On the other hand, during the early days of having PD, one of my biggest surprises with this disease was that I could rise above the limitations of my less-ability, at least for a while.

One of the early, most likely Parkinson's-related symptoms that began to limit what I could do as a guitarist involved the small-motor skills in my right, or picking, hand. It became harder to play, but I never really considered giving up the guitar. I wasn't getting better at it anymore and I had difficulty learning new music; nonetheless, I kept adjusting to the new normal, a full-time job because what seemed normal was a moving target.

One mixed blessing to come out of all this is that when I had to stop working in 2002 (I had been in book publishing for many years), my peculiar combination of circumstances (lots of free time, little stress) and the increasing rigidity of my right side encouraged me to focus less on instrumentals and more on words and storytelling. I began to write songs and lyrics, of which I'd done precious little. The results have ranged from pretty-darn-good to "It's still a little rough, honey," my wife's way of saying a song needs another trip through the mill.

Around this time, my neurologist suggested that I begin taking a dopamine agonist, ropinerole, the idea being that it would extend my "on" time when used in conjunction with levodopa. It performed as advertised, but my fine motor skills just didn't improve.

Trying to adjust, I kept my guitar accompaniments simple, like the basic one-two-three arpeggio I used in an original song whose lyrics are based on my meandering around the neighborhood with our old dog Barney three or four times a day. One thing that struck me on these walks was that the only other people outside on weekdays were moms pushing baby carriages. The song, "Mothers and Babies," works great without any fancy guitar work. Not every song can be adapted to downplay limited technique, but this one worked out.

I was taking ropinerole as part of my core medication regimen at this point. Then things started to fall apart.

The dopamine agonists gained brief notoriety a few years ago, when it was discovered that there was some evidence of a connection between use of this class of drugs and compulsive gambling, as well as other compulsive behaviors, such as shopping. The patients studied, in some cases, had never before set foot inside a casino, but suddenly felt compelled to do so. One thing was clear—people taking an agonist began to shell out money with abandon and without thinking through the consequences that could include financial ruin.

Oops.

Not surprisingly, this side-effect was not restricted to users of any single dopamine agonist but seemed to be characteristic of the entire class of medication.

I have been taking Requip (the brand name for the compound ropinerole) since 2000, around the time I began acting on the belief that I could actually make a little money buying, trading for, and selling vintage guitars. This turned into what could have been a disastrous outcome financially, undermining Lee's support and encouragement for me to find ways to continue playing music. As it was, my behavior resulted in my wife's significant concern for our finances and nearly precipitated an intervention when my friends and fellow musicians noticed I was behaving irrationally.

I am trying not to fool myself in what I say here. I was in fact addicted to spending money on expensive guitars. I told myself I had control over it, and what I was doing made perfect sense to me.

And it was quite an experience, being able to play great instruments: a Martin D-18 Golden Era; a 1951 Epiphone jazz box; a 1970s round-body Larrivee L-09 acoustic; a Roy Noble concert guitar with exotic hardwoods used for the sides and back; a bright-toned mahogany mid-80s Lowden, now owned by my older brother; a 1969 Gibson Country and Western guitar; a 1963 Gibson J-45; a 1968 Guild D-55; a light-blue 1981 special edition Fender Stratocaster; a lovely all-mahogany 1998 Martin 000-17S; a boomy 1996 Martin D-28 herringbone dreadnought; a 1949 Martin

000-18; a Taylor 355-series 12-string; a Taylor 810 dreadnought with deep, rich rosewood tone; and other fine guitars of similar quality and value.

It was like owning a premier guitar shop, as I was able to sample great instruments whenever I wanted to. But my "store" lost money with every transaction.

I bought, or traded for at a loss, another instrument every few months. If I couldn't sell something on craigslist or e-bay, I would consign it to a dealer trafficking in such goods so that I would have working capital to "reinvest." I always took a loss in this kind of selling agreement.

I lost track of how many instruments came and went through my house. I didn't keep clear records of the money in and out but I imagine that I lost around $10,000 over the course of a few years. I was addicted, pure and simple. Not that I can escape all responsibility for my actions, but after a little research and consultation with my neurologist, it appeared that I was suffering from side-effects of the drugs I was taking. The dopamine agonist ropinerole seemed to be contributing to my loss of self-control and to the ascendancy of poor judgment regarding my peculiar obsession with obtaining spendy guitars.

A contributing factor may have been that as my guitar-playing abilities became more of a problem because of Parkinson's disease, I actually believed I could find a guitar that could "play itself," even though I didn't let myself bring that conscious and clearly idiotic thought to the surface.

"This great little 1951 Martin 00-18 just might be the one," part of me would whisper to another part of me, so that I never exposed my irrationality to ridicule.

A collision of this belief, that I could find a guitar that

"played itself," and the reality that it was becoming impossible for me to play any guitar at all, was inevitable. I think what really put the brakes on the delusional thinking was the fact that I wasn't enjoying playing the guitar any longer. It just frustrated me. And I was put on a lower dose of Requip.

During the buying-selling episode, part of me was insane. I even downplayed the problem when I met with my psychiatrist, therapist, or neurologist. I was ashamed to admit that I was "hooked." It was something I didn't want to talk about, not even to myself.

I'm "clean" today. I at least know what the impulse to buy feels like, and thus I have better awareness of my options. I own one guitar and rarely cruise guitar shops or musical-instrument web sites anymore. That makes the same kind of common sense that a recovering alcoholic exhibits by wisely avoiding bars and taverns.

In 2006, I wrote in an issue of the *Parkinson Post*, "Parkinson's may have eroded my technical abilities on the guitar, and my fingers may have have lost their smooth motion. But I keep playing, even if it's not going well, because the only alternative is not to play, which would be a huge loss. I still can pick the guitar, which is an amazing thing. I think it's because the music in me is older than the Parkinson's, and my body knows the tune better than it knows the disease."

Those words are more upbeat than I currently feel.

By 2011, I had essentially given up playing the guitar. I had been giving it up for 10 years, even as I was swept up in the guitar-buying debacle, because playing was no longer fun. It's been a long process. I still take a small dose of Requip, which definitely improves motor function. But

Parkinson's has taken the music.

Whenever someone under 25 years old will listen to my advice, I tell them, "Don't doubt your talent, whatever it may be. It's a gift to share with others."

Because, really, anything can happen. Look at me. I'm learning the basic movement vocabulary of modern dance at 60, something I never would have imagined. I do pick up the guitar from time to time. It doesn't play itself, of course, but I can still make my way through a few chords before I start to stiffen up, lose heart, and put the guitar back in its case.

But as fate would have it, a friend of mine recently loaned me her Martin D-28 bluegrass guitar. Manufactured in the 1960s, when Martin still made the sides and backs of their guitars with Brazilian rosewood, the pre-1970 D-28 has a deep, powerful voice and ringing sustain. My friend told me I could borrow this beautiful instrument indefinitely.

Go figure.

I felt excited again, sitting up late that night and playing a great guitar obtained not through a compulsive purchase, but as a result of unexpected generosity. As I played, I felt my soul, if not my fingers, slip right into a groove that sounded a lot like music.

13.

Working for Free

The word *work* is so deeply embedded in our culture that when a restaurant waiter, eyeing my half-empty plate, asks me, "Are you still working on that?"—as if it were a chore to finish my meal—it makes me wonder what the word "work" really means to us, and why is it so often invoked?

Homework, housework, life's work, teamwork—all kinds of work.

We are part of an economic system that puts high value on work, especially when it is consistent with our social ethos. The most valued quality of work is still hard work that allows us to make an "honest" living. Asking someone what they do for a living is basically a way of sounding out relative value. But it is fascinating to know how much people are compensated for their time and energy. In physics, work and energy are related in ways that help scientists discover and explain laws of the physical universe. I don't think in our economic lives that energy and work have a clear connection. The amount of energy expended on work does not necessarily have a predictable influence on value. Many people can work casually or infrequently and still make a lot of money. And my idea of "a lot of money" may not be the same as yours.

Buddhists recognize that there is suffering everywhere, but, as the Vietnamese monk Thich Nhat Hahn points out, that does not mean that suffering is all there is.

In the same way, everybody works, or tries to work, but work is not all there is to life.

The last time I worked for a living was in May 2002. I'm not certain what to call my current work status. What is the opposite of working for a living? Living for a living? Living to work? Dying for a living?

I'd rather think of it as working for free, or working for a life. Working for free is not the same as working for nothing. The latter brings to mind slavery, indentured servitude, and existential despair. The concept of working for free, on the other hand, has a more positive feel. It could refer to volunteering, writing an opinion to your Congressperson, occupying Wall Street, composing music, or more generally following your interests and what seems important, and doing so without unreasonable financial expectations.

In late 2001 I was complaining to my neurologist about my work situation. I had cut back to four hours a day because of crushing fatigue and cognitive changes. The rest of the time I spent either girding up for or recovering from those four hours.

She said, "Today is as good as you're ever going to feel. Think about how you want to use your time and energy for the rest of your life."

Strong words. But it made me realize that I couldn't sustain the current picture. I had to make a change.

The next day I had a very difficult meeting with my boss of 14 years. He trusted me but didn't seem able to see my illness. I told him I had to leave. I still know that anyone who sees me at my best might, with good reason, think, "What's wrong with this guy? He looks fine to me."

The therapist I visited weekly at that time enthused

about how this was a great opportunity for me to realize whatever dream I had regarding what I could accomplish if I didn't "have to" work. Did he mean something like writing the Great American Novel, or becoming a staff photographer for *National Geographic*? God, I didn't need another career. I was incapable of having a career. That is why I had to stop working for a living.

I rolled this idea around my mental skating rink for a couple of weeks. Why didn't I have some monolithic goal to cross off the bucket list before I became too disabled to do anything? Such thoughts made me feel depressed and ashamed. Why didn't I have a clear, heroic ambition, like I imagined a normal person would have? How could I create a meaningful, enduring legacy? What was wrong with me?

Finally, I told my therapist that I had come to a realization: I didn't need a single "big thing" to take on, because I found peace, happiness, and a sense of accomplishment in simply following my lifelong interests: writing, playing the guitar, bicycling, having friends, going out for breakfast at the Old Town Cafe, enjoying the peace and stillness of the winter solstice, walking in the woods—the things I've always enjoyed doing.

I was 51 years old when I retired, still in what I consider the "grace period" of having Parkinson's—up to about five years post-diagnosis. I was not yet quite convinced that my limitations were real, or that disease progression did in fact apply to me. The meds were working pretty well. I wrote songs and took care of a neighbor's kids. I volunteered at the preschool that my then high-school-aged son had attended. I rode my recumbent trike, cared for and enjoyed a dog, a cat, and two pet rats. I had a good long-term disability insurance income. I had time.

How have I used it? I've extended myself more into the world, out there where it's a little scary sometimes. I've thought about what happens after we die, and what, if anything, lies on the other side of the veil. For all of our culture's apparent love affair with perpetual "connectedness," at least two great mysteries remain that won't be solved with additional bandwidth: the mysteries of birth and death. Why was I born to these people, in this place? What happens when I die?

I don't miss working for a living. The day I walked out of the office, I just left it behind and moved on. It actually surprised me. I thought I would experience a sense of loss, or confusion, or emptiness. Instead, it just felt like the right thing to do.

I've never looked back. Almost never.

I knew, barring miracles, that it was the last time I would ever work for a living. From that day I've been working for free. I have realized that work and accomplishment are compelling motivators in my life. I'm just in a different line of work now.

14.

Finding Hope on the Road

My wife Lee and I have been through some challenging times in our 27 years of marriage and friendship. We've also discovered some unexpected benefits and reasons for gratitude along the path toward living better with Parkinson's disease and rheumatoid arthritis. We wrote this piece together.

Rick: Somewhere between my Parkinson's diagnosis in 1998 and June 2008, I had forgotten what hope felt like. It didn't just disappear one day. It crept slowly, soundlessly away in the smallest increments during those past 10 years.

The realization came a few days after my first deep brain stimulation (DBS) surgery, while I was out walking with Lee. I noticed that my legs were springier and felt alive for the first time in years. I had been told that after implantation of my electrodes I might experience some dramatic but transient changes such as this.

The effect didn't last longer than a day, but it gave me hope that I would get back to the way I felt that day. And I dreamed of riding a bike again.

Lee: Rick has been riding bikes all his life, for commuting and for pleasure. In 1992, as he was commuting on his bike, he was broadsided by a car. It was after this accident that he first experienced neurological symptoms. In 1998 he was finally diagnosed with Parkinson's disease. I suspect the accident triggered the Parkinson's.

Rick: I'm uncomfortable when people tell me how brave I am to deal with Parkinson's disease in an active, upbeat way. The truth is, I am largely motivated by fear of disease progression and will do anything I can to stay otherwise healthy until the Next Great Thing in treatment comes along.

Lee: We happened to run into our friend Marilyn Williams, who is an avid cyclist and understands Parkinson's well. Her husband was diagnosed in 1996. She was telling Rick about her plans to ride with some friends from Bellingham to Glacier National Park in Montana, in July. Rick was truly excited for her and also, frankly, jealous. Rick told her that he had given up biking, but Marilyn asked, "What would it take to get you back on wheels?"

Rick: Things had been going in the wrong direction for a few years. Then, in June 2008, I had an epiphany: There was only one viable choice if I wanted to have a better-quality life. For me, deep brain stimulation surgery was the leap I had to make. It was the only game in town.

Lee: A couple of days later, Rick received a copy of an e-mail from Marilyn to Bill Bell, co-founder and executive director of the Northwest Parkinson's Foundation. Here's what it said:

> Rick has researched what it would take to start riding again. I will commit to rejoining Team Parkinson's and doing a serious job of fundraising if you will commit to getting Rick back on a bike. *—Marilyn*

Lee: With tears in his eyes, Rick shared this news with me and before we knew it, Marilyn had set up a page on the NWPF's Team Parkinson's web site.

I sent this information with an appeal for contributions out to friends and family. There was an immediate and overwhelming response. We were thrilled and really blown away!

Rick: On July 21, 2008, I had the first of two surgeries at Swedish Medical Center in Seattle, both performed by neurosurgeon Dr. Peter Nora. At the same time, we were fundraising for the recumbent trike, using the online Team Parkinson's fundraising format. The response was amazing: We hit our goal within a month.

Lee: By the time Marilyn headed to Mt. Rainier for her chosen Team Parkinson's fundraising ride (RAMROD, aka Ride Around Mt. Rainier in One Day), the fund had grown enough for Rick to shop. He found Mike Libik, who owns Easy Street Recumbents in Austin, Texas.

Rick: I chose a Sun X3 recumbent trike. The trike has a stable design, and Mike adapted it by installing a front-wheel hub motor and a lithium-ion battery pack.

Lee: Coincidentally, the trike arrived on the day we came home from Rick's second programming appointment to activate his DBS hardware.

Rick: Lee was the heart of the fundraising campaign, and she worked hard on it. My mood flagged occasionally, but our anticipation was keen.

I rode the trike home from the shipping dock, about a mile uphill. I panicked at first when my legs painfully seized up, but once I figured out the motor-assist function,

I relaxed and just accepted the extra power. The motor is virtually silent, and I pedaled and glided along the forest trail to our home near Lake Whatcom.

I know cycling and DBS aren't for everyone who has Parkinson's disease. But it was a miraculous time for me as I recaptured the hope I'd slowly lost. I'm looking forward to a great 2009, much of it in the saddle of the new trike. Thanks to everyone who made it happen.

2012 Update

The DBS procedure did not meet the expectations of my medical team. But my dyskinesias were dramatically reduced, almost gone. A hoped-for benefit—that I could reduce the amount of medication that I take—did not materialize. Programming is complicated by my sensitivity to the electrical stimulation. I need enough to get a therapeutic response. Over a certain line I experience violent and disabling dyskinesias.

In March 2010, I was hit by a truck while riding my trike in the bike lane down Cornwall Avenue. I didn't break bones, but my brain was rattled. Nightmares and paranoia lasted for several weeks. After I felt "normal" again, I decided my leg-powered and even my electric-assisted cycling days were over. I sold the trike to a friend in town who was recovering from a stroke. For me, the cars had won.

Now, although I drive the car on occasion to do errands in town, for the most part I get around on the city transit buses and on foot. It's a good way to travel.

15.

Speak No Evil

To be perfectly honest, I am a liar. I lie mostly to myself about what I think I need to have or to do to make me happy. It usually goes something like this: I affix my consciousness to an object I desire. Then, working backwards from the happiness I will surely feel when I have that object, I build an airtight custody case. My inner lawyer has just finished making a brilliant, impassioned summary speech to the jury and has convinced its members that the desire for the object is justified and that it constitutes a legitimate need. The jury votes unanimously in favor of the plaintiff, me. Bingo bango, I get my way!

I am a liar addicted to desiring new things, changes, people. Something grabs me by the gut every time I see a For Sale sign in a pickup truck or SUV along the road, or a pawn shop with an old guitar in the window. I have to stop and check it out. It might be a great deal! Maybe my wife will need some convincing, though. Just call in the jury and we'll try the case. Again.

Much to my undeserved benefit, her rulings are generally not in my favor.

Such, also, is my way of keeping my mind from becoming consumed with the progression of Parkinson's disease in my body.

People I know who have multiple sclerosis or Parkinson's disease admit to maintaining a certain level of denial. I call this "good denial," like good cholesterol. The bad kind might kill you.

For example, I have all these convoluted agreements and handshake deals with myself. Enough to make my head spin. "If this, then that." "If not this, then that anyway." "If not now, when?" "I legitimately need x, I'm not getting any younger, ergo, I get to have x."

This kind of messy thinking is a response to denial. Yet denial is a survival mechanism. It should be treated with respect.

Denial is sometimes the closest I can get to hope.

I love waiting for something I've purchased on the Internet to be delivered from the big FedEx truck. I have already concluded the jury trial on this one, and my anticipation, while intoxicating, produces anxiety. Should I have spent the money?

If I were smart, I would just skip the sweet anticipation of grace, cast out self-delusions about needing things, and start working on a sensible draft of my end-of-life directives.

I may be deemed a bad person for saying this, but I believe hope is overrated. Hope sounds so, well, helpless, like hoping there will be a cure for PD soon. I can hope all I want. The fact of the matter is, it either will or will not happen. That does not necessarily make me a pessimist. If I say the world is going to end tomorrow and it doesn't, I'm a pessimist (and a nut). If I say the world is going to end and the world ends, who cares about whether I am a pessimist, much less whether I was right? There's no upside to this attitude.

I lie so much about how this disease affects me, lies I tell to myself and others, that I find the path through the Parkinson's wilderness to be full of monsters and hidden traps. I keep thinking that there must be something beyond and within me that can free me from the hope paradigm. Because right now I mostly hope that I won't have to experience Parkinson's-related or any form of dementia. And I'm not sure I have the strength of faith to accept this possibility with equanimity and peace.

I am trying to find that connection between mind and heart to work through complicated matters: hope, faith, desire, addiction, and so on. I may not have faith in a cure for PD in my lifetime, but I do believe I can connect my intellect and my emotions, my ideas and my feelings, my fears and my strengths during the years I have left.

I said that I wouldn't give advice in this book. I lied. My advice is to be kinder to yourself and to other people and express gratitude daily for the gifts you've been given. The writer John Barth once said (through one of his fictional characters) that "self-knowledge is always bad news." I have come around to where I disagree with that sort of bad faith.

Know thyself. Tell no lies. Do no harm. Speak no evil. Hope for the best. Have faith in the universe.

16.

The Spirits of Dead Horses

My worst nightmare became reality yesterday afternoon. While driving to the store, I hit a bicycle rider. The only not-horrible part of the story, if there is a part that is not horrible, is that the contact was "low-impact." That's like saying to someone who has been rescued from a house fire with only second-degree burns, "It could have been worse." Sure, but the fact remains that I hit a girl on a bike with my car. However you look at it, the car's driver is the responsible party. I've been the one lying in the street before, and I know that there is no minimizing the harm done when a pedestrian or cyclist is struck by a car.

Our car has good brakes, thank God. Both a paramedic and the police officer on the scene told me the girl on the bike was going to be okay. I had to believe them.

I write elsewhere in this book about being in the cyclist's position in a car-bike encounter. Is what happened yesterday Karma? I'm serious. Or, have I used up my portion of luck as a PWP behind the wheel? How do people with Parkinson's disease know when driving is no longer safe? Hitting a girl on a bike might be the signal for me to give those questions some consideration. Would I have been able to stop in time if my reaction time wasn't compromised by the disease?

This story, however, is not about what happened yesterday, even though I can't get the collision out of my thoughts. My story begins with something that happened long ago.

In the winter of 1970–1971, a barn recently built on my mother's and step-dad's hobby farm caught fire. It had started with sparks shooting from an electrical short in a wire that powered heat lamps to keep my step-dad's goddamn pigs warm. The cedar building, full of dry hay, burned to the ground.

Away at college, I heard about the fire by a letter from my mother. For years, I've blocked the content of that letter from my conscious mind. There were three horses who died in the fire and for 35 or so years I've kept the pain from that horrible news hidden deep. Over the past few years it has come back to me, with feelings of horror, guilt, anger, shame, and remorse, even though I wasn't actually there when it happened.

We had moved from southern California in 1967 to take ownership of ten acres on Whidbey Island. I was in high school. The three of us—Mom, my step-father, and me— had no idea how little we knew about the needs of the animals we began to acquire.

But let me leave those ashes on the dark, wet ground where the barn had stood and move forward, beyond my mother's ashes, beyond my step-father's ashes, beyond the soil thrown over the casket that held my father's body in a grave on a hillside near Chino, California, beyond my sister's losing her life to cancer in 2010.

A few years ago, I realized that I wanted to ride horses, again, for more than one reason. I had taken riding lessons with my son Eli when he was in middle school. We both enjoyed doing something together that was out of the ordinary. We practiced in an arena that was part of a boarding stable, riding Western style. Both before and after each session, we cross-tied our horses in the breezeway of the main barn, and then we rubbed them down, groomed their coats, and cleaned their hooves. We kept up with the lessons until Eli moved on to other things; it remains a good memory for me.

Arena riding is intense, with many variables that quickly change value whenever you ask the horse to change gait, turn, back up, or stop. We didn't get outside much with the horses in that class. So I jumped at the chance to book a half-day trail ride with a local outfitter when we were visiting friends in the beautiful Methow Valley near the town of Mazama, Washington.

We did the morning ride on a warm day in June. Once we got oriented and were given basic instructions, Lee, Eli, and I found ourselves in our saddles, being led down the trail by a cute-as-could-be former Apple Blossom Queen from Wenatchee mounted on her beautiful dark-coated horse, up into the hills that rise from the valley floor. She talked most of the way, but it was all interesting stuff about horses and the country and cowboys and graduating from high school in eastern Washington, and then more about horses. As we sat on a rocky outcrop, our horses tethered back in the trees, I looked out at the valley and the mountains beyond and at the clouds being moved around by the wind, and everything fit and was right. Just for that moment, I felt closer to the center of the mystery and wonder of life.

It might be obvious that I like horses. I like being in the saddle riding, trying to communicate with the magnificent animal who holds me above the earth. But now, because of Parkinson's disease, I have poor balance. This creates both a challenge and an opportunity for joyous adventure. I took this opportunity to improve my balance, and to find out whether I could still ride.

There are paths other than horseback riding to help restore balance. Tai-chi, for example, helps me maintain my equilibrium, but I don't practice often enough. I've read that horseback riding has similar benefits and for me it's more fun than tai-chi. Sound, functional limbs, however, are also requirements for a successful rider. I have some deficits in those areas. But no problem: I wasn't trying to train for competition. I just wanted to have an enjoyable experience.

I tried riding again more recently. This time, Eli was away at college in Montana.

During my brief search for a suitable stable, I noticed that most student riders at stables in Whatcom County are pre-teen and teenage girls. I'm not sure exactly what that's all about, but the stable owner I chose to oversee my lessons was delighted to have an adult, a male no less, with Parkinson's disease to boot, wanting to take riding lessons. This ranch family owned their own horses and used them for lessons. They did not board any horses, which gave them the advantage of knowing that their stock remained healthy and in good working order.

I started riding in the arena with a leaky roof on a rainy Tuesday in November, trying out three or four different mounts over the next month to check temperament and fit.

After a few lessons I was allowed to ride a very special horse: a Dutch Warmblood mare, black except for small splotches of white on her chest. In the summer I saw dark chocolate brown in her fur. She used to be a jumper. Her name is Saffron, and I've missed her since the stable relocated to property too far from home for me to drive.

She was fairly aloof at first. During the year or so that I rode Saffy, however, she began to know me pretty well and did things her owner had rarely seen her do for a new rider, like following me around the arena without a lead and letting me touch the underside of her chin. And I didn't have any of the nightmarish feelings about the memory of the burning barn when I was riding Saffron. She allowed me time to learn some of what she knew. She was my teacher. She kept the spirits of dead horses from haunting me.

Now the hauntings come in slow-motion replays of hitting the girl on the bike, of her vulnerability, the vulnerability we all experience at times. At least I do. As I become less physically adept and less able to deal with the everyday world, I have to concede freedom of movement as I once knew it. My limitations are real.

I think it is time to stop driving the car. I doubt I could live with myself if another person were to be hurt as a result of my inattentiveness or slowed reaction time due to having this insidious illness.

17.

The Tortoise and the Aerialist

From the darkened stage, the sound of a chair being dragged on the wooden floor is heard. Footsteps move toward the still-invisible chair. Then silence. The lights begin slowly to come up, like dawn on a day without clouds, and I see a young woman the same stature of an Olympic gymnast standing on a chair underneath a trapeze bar suspended by ropes to an invisible point somewhere high above the stage. Now there appears a young man who lifts the aerialist by the hips, from where she is standing, straight up, so that she can grab the bar with two hands. Then the young man walks offstage, taking the chair with him.

I don't really know the young trapeze artist, Shannon Gray Collier. Our time in face-to-face conversation totals maybe 10 minutes. She was born about five years prior to my first Parkinson's symptoms in 1992. I'm old enough to be her grandfather.

We met by accident one weekend when we both showed up at a modeling session for a painting class. The instructor, a well-known artist in the community, had double-booked us.

Trying to be fair and make the best of the situation, the instructor invited us to work as a duo.

A duo indeed. Honestly, I had never posed for a painting

in my life and relied on Shannon to choreograph our positions. It was work, but it went pretty well. I think everyone in the class had a productive and enjoyable session, thanks mostly to Shannon's inventiveness. She made this aging tortoise feel like he was on a guided adventure to a new country. I enjoyed the ride, but when I stepped back outside, I was still on Cornwall Avenue in Bellingham, Washington. So I was trying something new. Why not?

"While I say that I'm a circus artist," Shannon explains, "it's just putting rather insignificant words to a much greater exploration and passion. Really, my true goal in life is to reach a simple peace within myself and to share beauty with the world."

I had just published my first book, a collection of short stories, and there is one story that I felt could be developed into a longer piece. Initially, I wrote that the main character, 10-year-old Shush McCrea, aspired to be a human cannonball. Her mother has multiple sclerosis, and carried around unfinished business from a liaison with an undependable circus wrangler, which was over long before Shush was born.

I thought about how Shannon would be the perfect person to interview as the basis for expanding the character and the story. Shush would grow up and at age 25 be working as an aerialist at Cirque du Soleil-type performance venues.

Shannon, a real circus performer who spends most of her time shuttling between San Francisco and Montreal, agreed to be interviewed, ostensibly as the basis for my character's development. I wanted ideas about how Shush McCrea ends up working as a circus performer and how she feels about her life.

I wrote up a list of prompts to get Shannon started and sent them to her in an e-mail, since she was about to leave for San Francisco to perform.

On the stage, hanging from the suspended bar, Shannon begins to perform, but her expressive soul-bearing movement vocabulary goes beyond what the word "performance" can describe. Her movements require the strength of an Olympic ring gymnast.

I wrote to Shannon on Dec. 8, 2011, "I did get the first installment of your answers and read it through more than once."

She had written about her teen years when she was a sports jock, a star multi-sport athlete in high school. She remembered the chink-by-chink collapse of her identity as a competitor, and how that set her on a different path. Reading four or five pages of her long, cramped, single-spaced paragraphs, I realized that this was the real story, Shannon's story. And I had no idea what to do with it.

"During my senior year [of high school]," Shannon continued, "part way through the basketball season, in the unbearable cold of Wisconsin winter, I felt like I had lost all control of my life, of my ability to play, of my body. Without even realizing it at the time, I started to develop an eating disorder that would completely consume me for the next three years of my life."

I remember pursuing answers with the kind of intensity that Shannon described when I was in my late teens and early to mid-twenties. I still don't even know all the questions.

Shannon's writing put me back on Whidbey Island

at Langley High School, drafted for the basketball team because I was the tallest kid in the school. Doing well as a high school player, I went on to college at Washington State University with an invitation from the basketball coach to try out as a walk-on. The coach was disappointed when I told him two weeks into practices that I couldn't do sports and academics at the same time. He said, "You were one of the guys who looked good enough in scrimmage to have a shot at making the team." I still think I made the right decision, but who knows what awaits down the road not taken.

I too developed an eating disorder and lost 40 pounds by the end of my second semester.

She is an amazing artist. The flow of her routine, which uses the bar and ropes as an extension of her body, seems flawless. I can't hear anyone in the audience breathing.

Shannon: "I am often plagued with an unrelenting sense of anxiety and detachment in my everyday life, always striving for something more, to be doing and creating everything I possibly can. This constant drive and incredible pressure I put myself under has led me to achieve really neat things in short amounts of time, but also leads to complete burnout as with my sports in high school. I think underlying this drive is simply an attempt to quench a feeling of lacking, lacking presence I suppose. Or trying to find purpose in my life."

We are two very different people, Shannon and I, and yet we find a connection on some level. Was it coincidence that we both showed up to be painted on that afternoon in Bellingham? This may be the story I really wanted, while I thought I was looking for something completely different. Maybe it has to do with my own recent efforts to dance expressively, Parkinson's notwithstanding. My dance teacher keeps challenging me, which is good, and I have grown as a dancer during the past year and a half of classes. Will you ever see me perform a grand jeté? When pigs fly.

One more piece of Shannon Gray Collier's young life:

"When I move, I tell my whole story. Someone once told me after a performance, 'You dance like your life depends on it,' and in a way, my life did depend on it. I like finding movement in its purest source, with no pressure, expectations, or fear. Movement leads me to find my self again. I dance my truth and when I perform, I try to share this place. Sometimes it's painful, and sometimes it's completely joyous, but it's always honest."

18.

Disabled or Not Disabled: What Was the Question?

Often when we drive downtown for a concert, a movie, or just some meandering, my wife is reluctant to use the disabled parking spots, even though we have the blue disabled-parking card that we hang on the rear view mirror to indicate that we can legally use such spots. I tend to live in various states of disability, so sometimes it is fine with me to park a little further from our destination. Other times, if there are no regular parking spaces available anywhere in the surrounding acre of parking lot, we might use one of the disabled spots.

Such situations make me feel like I may not really be disabled. I don't know if my wife feels the same way, though she has had disabling rheumatoid arthritis for more than 25 years. Together we can tote up 46-plus years of disability, yet here we are, still thinking that there might be a *really* disabled person who deserves that special parking spot with the blue and white sign on which the image of a person in a wheelchair clearly implies that if you can stand up and walk, you must not be too disabled.

Years ago I coined the word *less-ability* to describe my early years after diagnosis, partly because I realized that there were people out there with Parkinson's a lot worse off than me and partly because I was still working and held the illusion that I, not the disease, would determine if and when I stopped working.

Nowadays I sit quietly whenever a recently diagnosed PWP says something blustery about determining one's fate with Parkinson's. I thought initially that I had four to five good working years ahead of me following my diagnosis. Two years later, however, I hit the wall and couldn't do my work any longer.

I never discourage anyone from trying to find hope using any resources he or she may have at his or her disposal. But I have experienced firsthand that Parkinson's moves at its own pace, not necessarily at the pace one wishes.

I just talked to my friend Meggan, who has constant pain throughout her body and has tried just about any treatment intervention available to help her get through the day. Today, on the winter solstice, Meggan had made the decision not to accompany Lee and me to our favorite annual solstice ceremony because it involves alternately lying on the floor, sitting on one's knees, twirling on one's feet in a crush of people, and dancing ecstatically.

Meggan's body would pay dearly if she engaged in the activity.

She said, "I've decided to stay home and try to take care of the body I have."

Limitations are bitter pills to swallow.

It really used to bother me when someone would ask me about my Parkinson's symptoms, and then dismissively comment that they too had fatigue in the afternoon like all normal working people or that they also felt stiff in the morning, especially if they had just knocked out a half-marathon after work the previous day, or that they had balance problems when they drank a lot of alcohol. I'm not making this up.

The punch line is always, "And I don't have Parkinson's disease."

But that's just the point. No, you don't have Parkinson's disease. I do.

Questions that don't interest me very much: who gets Parkinson's and why? Who does not get Parkinson's? I really don't know. To ask, "Why me?" poses a question no one but God can answer, if there is a God.

The question of why Parkinson's manifests in people at all is more productive. These are my thoughts. An answer to the question, "Who am I?" is in part realizing that I am an individual "specimen" of *homo sapiens,* a work in progress while evolutionary forces are still working out the kinks we call illness, such as cancer, insanity, heart failure, multiple sclerosis, ALS, Parkinson's disease, macular degeneration, and so on. Although we separate and categorize and break illnesses down into finer and finer domains of specialization, the simple fact is that evolutionary forces are still "working" on us. It ain't perfect yet, and may never be so.

As well, the mere fact that we have "survived" evolution to this point is no guarantee that evolution will do anything that we expect. I've heard my brother talk about "really evolved" spiritual people. But evolution does not happen to an individual. Evolution is another answer to the question characterized in recent foodie books as the omnivore's dilemma: which group of similar life forms can adapt most quickly to avoid being eaten by the next up-food-chain diners?

Evolution is past tense. It is the principle and energy that over millions of years of eating and being eaten has resulted in our current world, with all its joys and woes. And there is no guarantee that of the seven billion people currently occupying the planet even one will survive—or two, a man and a woman, of course, to replant the Garden.

Now, what was the question? Something about finding parking that doesn't use a disabled driver spot. Because my wife (and sometimes I) believe that spot might be needed by someone who is *really* disabled.

19.

The Tortoise Dances

Because, really, there is not much left to do—or so the tortoise thought, in his tortoise-like way.

Out here in the middle of the ocean, on my island refuge, I dance for the red-footed boobies and the blue-footed boobies, for the iguanas, for the egrets and herons, for the mute cacti, the Sally-lightfoot crabs, for the mockingbirds and lizards. Dance the only dance I know, the one I perform to rid myself of demons and monsters whose scaly sloughed skin has encrusted my body and dreams. It is time to give hope new life, let it wander, Siddhartha-like, to see the suffering beyond the safe haven of home, yet still find joy in spite of suffering.

From the edge of a rock cliff on the south-facing end of Cap Sante in Anacortes, Washington, the view is spectacular. But the heart is sad and heavy with grief that can hardly be articulated. I have spoken with the shamans about this. All have differing opinions, but I think the strain of the past week has been made worse by the new Parkinson's drug I started taking a couple weeks ago. It appears to create havoc either on its own or in the way it interacts with the antidepressant medications I take. Uncontrollable sobbing comes in sets like the ocean waves, crashing against the rocks and then retreating for a period of emotionally flat calm.

The shamans speak in different languages as they try to expose and chase the darkness from the heart of the tortoise.

There are still no dogs on the island. They would become feral and do significant environmental damage if left to their own devices, so I keep them off.

I believe I mainly wanted a dog because I like dogs. It really didn't have to be a service dog, but getting a trained dog through a certified assistance-dog organization was something good to look forward to. And I need things to look forward to.

Not many Parkinson's patients that I have come across have service dogs. I think that may be because our symptoms and drug side-effects go through a number of cycles every day; as opposed, perhaps, to someone who is in a wheelchair or electric scooter because he or she has lost leg function and might have needs that are more consistent from day to day. I don't know, because I have never been confined to a wheelchair. But the wheelchair has really become the symbol of disability because it is clear that the occupant of the chair on wheels is in fact unable to walk, and is thus disabled.

Parkinson's makes me unpredictable. I freeze in the early morning and often in the evening, and at unpredictable hours I get wobbly on my feet. I met a H.O.P.E. (an annual Parkinson's conference in Seattle) attendee a couple years ago who had trained his own dog to help him with tasks of some sort. Maybe he was able to train the dog effectively for his particular symptoms. But even a trained dog is still and foremost a dog, and dogs are instinctive, unapologetic opportunists, ready to test your mettle and pluck at your most vulnerable heartstrings to get a response. Any response.

And so recently I wandered innocently into one of the more difficult weeks of my life. The team training program for becoming a certified disabled dog handler was scheduled for the two weeks right before Christmas, from 10:00 in the morning until 5:00 in the afternoon for 10 workdays. Our commute to Anacortes took about an hour, each way. In the middle of the first week we began bringing Finn home with us, and he stayed with us over the weekend. He was very calm, but I was having a nervous-system meltdown. I simply could not cope, and between periods of crying I wondered where this malaise was coming from. My acute emotional turmoil didn't match the circumstances. There were adjustments to be made, things to move around in the house. But my reaction involved something more than was warranted by these activities. I began to notice that the sobbing episodes came in waves. I suspected a medication incompatibility.

Finn is tall enough to rest his muzzle on the kitchen counters, his tail capable of wagging cups and vases right off the coffee table or scattering loose papers to the far corners of the room. That's why we moved things. He is almost all black, a surprising outcome because his parents are a yellow Lab and a long-haired Collie. When he stretched out on a pad or on the carpet at our house, his straight long legs, both front and back, came together at his paws. The result was an equilateral triangle of dog. I think he has sad eyes, but that is probably just my projection. He is slow-moving but could also prance like a puppy if there was a game to play.

He is a sweet dog.

I knew, however, even before I allowed the thought to be unlocked, that this wasn't going to work.

I said to one of the shamans that getting a dog was like taking our already compromised, stretched-to-the-limit lives and dropping an 85-pound, two-year-old dog into the mix, thinking that would make life easier, or somehow better. It's similar to the flawed logic used by a young married couple who, when they hit a rough patch, believe that having a baby will bring them back into marital harmony.

On Monday of the second week, I told Summit that I could not continue. They understood, I think. I'm not sure I even understood. Then Lee drove me up to the top of Cap Sante, where I gazed out at the world from a more elevated perspective.

We later returned the leash, food and water bowls, a small bag of food, containers of glucosamine and fish oil capsules, and the old pad that Finn liked to sleep on. I ran an ad for the kennel on craigslist. I felt overwhelmed by the weight of the shell I wear around myself as protection from emotional predation.

I am a slow but flowing dancer, and I at times feel as though I am free from the armor I wear to keep my heart from breaking. When a tortoise dances, the dance comes from his most vulnerable places, but he will never leave the shell.

In the end, this episode resolved quietly, the deep sadness growing tolerable. I stopped taking the suspect PD medication. I spoke to and worked with the shamans. I'm not sure whose potions let me return to my island state of peace. Something worked. I got better.

After all this, in some crazy way I know that I would not be dancing on the sand if I didn't have Parkinson's disease, or if I never had any opportunities to feel deep loss. Of a dog. Of my health.

20.

"I Don't Mind What Happens"

Tonight is New Year's Eve, 2011. Friends from Seattle are coming up to Bellingham, not to revel with us, but to eat dinner together, after which they will head down to the Sons of Norway Hall for a New Year's Eve contra dance. It sounds like something Garrison Keillor's fictional characters might do on a slow evening in Lake Wobegon. They change clothes after dinner, putting on what I guess constitutes typical Northwest contra-dancing regalia. Kristin's twirling skirt and sleeveless black top, Jeff's baggy multicolored shorts that look as if they were made from silk, and a cool, illustrated T-shirt over which an unbuttoned Hawaiian shirt hangs.

Lee and I are tired, more tired than we want to be. We are spending tonight trying to talk about what we learned during the past year, and what our goals are for 2012. This can be a very difficult thing to do—I can barely remember what I did yesterday. But we get into a real conversation, more about fears than about hope. The goals I am taking on for the coming year include gaining clarity about what is important, and to be more loving and helpful to other people, starting at home. But underneath that is a layer of doubt and uncertainty that makes goals wither and enfeebles the resolve necessary to make changes in my life.

The truth is, I am sitting here next to the fireplace writing, and that seems quite enough to ask. I am perfectly content and grateful for my life at this moment.

People who practice certain forms of meditation and spiritual exploration have said that given the peculiar structure of time and reality, this moment is really all that we have. And for a moment there, gone in a wink, I existed without Parkinson's disease. When I noticed and marked the "moment," Parkinson's returned. I'm not sure it "went" anywhere, or if there is an "anywhere" to which it could go, whether I dream about PD or whether Parkinson's dreams about me.

During a talk given by the spiritual teacher J. Krishnamurti a few years ago, someone in the audience wrote a question on a piece of paper that was handed to Krishnamurti. The teacher said, "This person has written, 'Who are you?'" Pause. Reflecting on this before replying, Krishnamurti finally said, "The question is not very interesting. The question that is interesting and that you should be asking yourself is 'Who Am I?' Because to you, I may appear to be somebody great sitting up here. But I am nobody. It's as very simple as that."

The way we frame our view of the world, the words we use to tell the story, are part of what we perceive. Krishnamurti was quoted in Eckhart Tolle's book *A New Earth* as saying, "I don't mind what happens."

I found that idea useful as I prepared for my DBS surgery in July of 2008. It was a way to detach from the importance of the outcome. Notice that Krishnamurti doesn't say, "I don't *care* what happens," or that what happens will not cause suffering. He is saying, I think, that he has opened himself to life's experience with equanimity and acceptance. To "not mind" is simply to withhold judgment about one's suffering.

And so Lee and I find ourselves sitting in our living room being warmed by the flames licking from our natural gas fireplace. I didn't like this fireplace at first; I saw it as being "fake." Now I view it as a helpful convenience that warms me up when I'm cold. Calling anything fake is judgment that doesn't tell me anything about the nature of what we're describing. The fake flowers in the vase can still be beautiful, even a work of art in their own way. Fake candles that are actually soft, electricity-powered bulbs, when placed in the windows on cold winter nights, bring a genuine feeling of warmth and welcome to those who pass by.

We seem to enjoy making things that imitate "real" life, but what is so *real* about real life?

As I have been engaged in the process of creating this book, I feel that in one sense I have been so focused on Parkinson's disease and the way it manifests in my life that I have put a strain on the equilibrium I try to maintain with the disease. Christine, one of my support group friends, said back in the autumn that she was planting tulip bulbs for a Parkinson's awareness project, helping to promote a singing program that helps people with PD, participating in twice-a-week Dance for PD classes, and attending our PD support-group meetings, as well as dealing with her symptoms. All her activities became constant reminders that she has Parkinson's disease.

I know what she is saying, but while preoccupation with illness is sometimes useful and sometimes interfering, the focus and act of writing takes me outside "my" Parkinson's.

I am not a "person with Parkinson's disease writing." I am simply a person writing about Parkinson's disease, a topic with which I am familiar.

Every morning I get out of bed to live my life. Some days I remember to be grateful, and some days I just can't see what the point of all this might be. Hope comes in gusts, quick breezes here and there. For me, it is not a continuous state of being.

I "hope" people read and get something out of my rustic musings. But I'm not in a position to influence others' actions or preferences. I believe, as another option, that cultivating a feeling of calmness can create an attitude that might better accommodate disappointment when hopes are dashed, whether or not one is living with Parkinson's disease. Speaking as someone who does live with PD, I know that every day brings change, which we regard as either good or bad. It would be hardhearted not to have compassion for a person or family going through a difficult transition, telling them that hope is irrelevant.

Maybe if we combined the word *hope* with the attitude "I don't mind what happens," acceptance of the outcome of an illness would entail less suffering, and hope might make the journey sweeter.

I don't know. I have no answers to offer.

But if you are living with Parkinson's disease, I hope that every day brings you a fresh idea or the gust of a warm breeze that makes the journey easier.

21.

Self-Healing?

The phenomenon of spontaneous healing has probably been around as long as *homo sapiens* has inhabited the planet. Early humans certainly didn't have sophisticated technology or double-blind drug trials. Their approach was closely integrated into the web of Nature and superstitious or magical beliefs that guided their actions. I am not sure what healing looked like 200,000 years ago, but I suspect that there is a link between finding out which plants and roots helped one member of a tribal group get well and the modern medical technique called the *differential diagnosis* (see Glossary), which proceeds by incrementally eliminating possible disease types and arriving at a diagnosis that supports the clinical findings. It is an ingenious, effective method that is at the heart of every episode of the television show *House*.

But back to history.

By the end of the 18th century, Western culture marked the ascent of modern science and the creation of independent scientific disciplines. Now, in today's world, we can easily line up the rationalist skeptics—those who believe that modern science comprises the only valid paradigm—on one side of the fence and, on the other, those who believe that healing can take place without visible cause let alone without the corroboration of scientific evidence.

Dr. Andrew Weil, an MD who popularized the practice of integrative medicine, has even written a book on this topic, *Spontaneous Healing*. I'm sure he is not the only one who has weighed in on this developing area.

Why am I bringing this up? Because I am caught between a belief in miracles and a sort of empirical agnosticism. I'm in agreement with Hamlet when he says to Horatio that "there are more things in heaven and earth ... than are dreamt of in your philosophy" (Act I, Scene 5). But I am suspicious of some "miracles" because I grew up in and still inhabit a culture that is uncomfortable with anything we can't see. Our culture marginalizes the miraculous and exiles it into the realm of fantasy.

Call me a spontaneous-healing agnostic.

Going back to Western Civilization's primary religious source material (courtesy of Google), I find in the *Bible* that Jesus healed the sick and dying on a regular basis. In the books of Matthew, Mark, Luke, and John, there are 27 passages describing the healing miracles of Jesus. I'm not a biblical scholar (or even a Christian), but I don't recall anyone besides Jesus healing the sick and dying. Nor does any biblical figure heal himself.

What does all this have to do with Parkinson's disease?

If you haven't heard of John Coleman, then you should read his book *Stop Parkin' and Start Livin'*. You should make up your own mind whether he is a living example of a self-healing process or a nut. Or something in between.

Coleman, who claims he was diagnosed with PD and multiple-system atrophy (MSA) in 1995, says he used homeopathy, something called aqua-hydration therapy, Bowen therapy, craniosacral therapy, flower essences, counseling, meditation, and spiritual development to heal himself. Coleman claims that as a result of creating and following a strict regimen, he became completely symptom free by April 1998.

Some questions occur to me.

Is his story a remarkable case of self-healing?

Did Coleman actually have Parkinson's disease and MSA, as he claims?

Did he intend to create a package he can sell (his book and the regimen he spells out) that is based on whatever he had or had not experienced?

I don't know the answers. I'm not going to spend any time trashing Coleman, because I don't think he deserves it. Others have already done their best to discredit the Australian self-proclaimed self-healer. I am hesitant to join in the general negativity of his detractors because most of the therapies he uses are consistent with what I think constitute a reasonable integrative medical approach to any chronic illness.

Being chronically ill, we have to be good detectives, following up on all leads, even if some of them lead nowhere. This effort takes significant time and resources. When someone like Coleman comes along, I feel compelled to follow his lead and turn down the volume on my inner skeptic.

I must frequently remind myself that my only relevant expertise is in having Parkinson's disease, not in curing it or reversing its symptoms without the benefit of modern medications and surgical interventions. That's the world in which I'm living. I use what really works.

Some people live in a different world, and I honestly respect that. But it is hard enough to have PD without feeling remiss or lazy about not taking advantage of someone's recipe for self-healing. Considering the job of self-healing makes me tired.

My experience with Parkinson's disease has involved taking prescribed medications that mitigate symptoms, undergoing DBS surgery to add electrical stimulation to targeted brain regions that control movement, and doing my best to otherwise stay as healthy and as mentally and physically active as I can. That's my path. Some choose another path.

Regarding the fence that seems to divide us: those of us with PD each try to find a path to healing even if it doesn't include being cured of the disease. Maybe there is really no fence between us. After all, we are all self-healers to a large extent, thanks to our miraculous self-defense network, the immune system. If we didn't have self-healing mechanisms coded into our DNA, we all would have died of the common cold or a simple infection long ago. Our bodies can self-regenerate up to a point. Where is that point? Has John Coleman traveled beyond it and opened up a new chapter in the treatment of Parkinson's disease?

22.

Into the Woods

I've been reading a book about the Tarahumara, a secluded indigenous society whose members live in the vast Copper Canyon of the Sierra Occidental in Mexico. The Tarahumara are legendary long-distance runners who spend a lot of their time running hundred-mile routes for the sheer joy of moving through the world they occupy. Not training, just running. Theirs is an inspiring though ultimately tragic story that actually changed my attitude about walking, a form of exercise that is still available to me.

My history of walking for joy probably began when I lived in Pullman, Washington, a university town near the Idaho border, from 1969 through 1972. I spent hours out walking the wooded creek bottoms and back roads of the country referred to as the Palouse (pronounced Puh-loose). In autumn, after harvest, the monochromatic fields lay fallow. In the spring, the new growth stuck up out of the soil like stubble on a man's unshaved face. I walked tirelessly. While on the outskirts of the town, I frequently went bouldering on the escarpments of extrusive basaltic rock that broke up the smooth hills of the fertile topsoil.

Living with Parkinson's, I get tired. But I can still just walk out the door and onto the park trails, after making sure I have included the ten essentials in my backpack: water, an apple, cell phone, light rain jacket, carbidopa-levodopa, amantadine, Wellbutrin, gloves, and ropinerole. Maybe a peanut-butter sandwich.

I have rediscovered and adopted the perspective that to move under my own power is a joy, be it running or walking. I feel privileged and fortunate to be able to walk five miles on a good day, even with some altitude thrown in.

Today's gray cover of clouds with occasional rain typifies October-through-May conditions in Bellingham. In fact, it is late January, exactly a month after the winter solstice.

Starting out from home around two in the afternoon a few weeks ago, I walked the park trail along the north bank of Whatcom Creek, all the way to the commemorative totem pole honoring the three local boys who were killed in the Olympic pipeline explosion in 2001, a cataclysmic event that changed and strengthened national pipeline safety regulations.

Rather than running under a blue sky across a savagely beautiful landscape in Mexico, however, I found myself crossing the roiling waters of Whatcom Creek on a recently constructed bridge near the memorial totem pole. I wanted to make a loop around the cemetery to get home but changed my mind when I saw a couple in yellow rain jackets heading straight up the hill towards the woods. I thought, the Waterline Trail is up in that direction. I knew parts of the trail and was sure it would lead me home.

For some reason, maybe paranoia, I feel more secure seeing "normal" people, as opposed to scary-looking people, ahead of me on a woodland trail. So I followed the couple, brightly visible in their reassuring yellow raincoats, surely purchased from REI, up into the woods that muffled car noise from the street far below me.

The couple, 30 or 40 yards ahead of me, suddenly walked around a bend and disappeared. I lost them, or they lost me.

I knew where I was, sort of. In the woods on the south side of the creek, following a zig-zagging trail that wandered like it couldn't make up its mind where it was going. Following a false lead downhill, because I saw a trail heading up the next hill, I slipped and fell on my butt in the mud. Had I not stopped thus, I could have been in trouble. Having slid down the mud-slick hill a few feet, I saw and heard the fast-running cold waters of Whatcom Creek, which I hadn't seen from higher up, between the hill on which I stood and the next one over.

It was beginning to grow dark early, even though it was still too early by the clock for the light to be fading. The days here are short enough as it is in January. Clouds and rain just make them feel shorter.

It's difficult for me to see in the dusky gloom and almost impossible in near-darkness. So I was getting mildly concerned. I felt vulnerable to the dark, worried about the disorientation I was experiencing, the head-spinning sensation that comes to me during strenuous physical activity, and my sore wrist with which I had tried to check my fall in the mud. The woods, as I followed the track again, the trees, stumps, the moss, the boggy, brambly wetland all seemed to take on a new, darkening menace.

This was not exactly *Into the Wild,* Jon Krakauer's story of a young man who ventures into the Alaskan bush and dies when he accidentally eats poisonous berries that resemble a benign, nutritious variety. Cut off from help by a raging river, weak, sick, and unable to eat, he starves to death in the winter cold, inside an abandoned school bus in which he had lived during the summer.

Nor was it a chapter out of Christopher McDougall's book, *Born To Run,* about a group of quirky American ultra-runners in a cross-country race with the Tarahumara Indians through an area that is inhospitable and sparsely populated. To boot, they were under constant threat of running afoul of a Mexican drug cartel that plants its crop of marijuana in remote, fiercely guarded fields among the mountains and canyons of the Sierra Madre.

I wasn't even outside the Bellingham city limits.

Although I suppose the unease I experienced in the woods could have been felt by anyone, I was panicking only a mile or two from home—partly, I think, because of my (imagined?) predicament, but mostly because my Parkinson's brain, short on dopamine and crowded with various neurological and psychiatric medications, was trying unsuccessfully to get a handle on my present situation. Disability magnifies problems that might otherwise seem to be routine.

I survived.

More recently, I set out one morning, walking through Whatcom Falls Park and up a dead-end street, at the end of which I found a marker identifying the Galbraith Mountain trail system. This area is a maze of single-track bike routes that all seemed to be going downhill, as I struggled to gain elevation.

I dug in with my trekking poles, mentally ticking off my ten essentials, minus the peanut-butter sandwich, in the daypack I had strapped on. At home I'd been coffeed, fed, and pilled like a thoroughbred horse before a big race, my brain filled with stuff that'd make make me work better.

During the summer, mountain bikers fly down these twisting and turning trails, but in mid-February I was alone, and this was my first time on the mountain. It took me an hour climbing switchbacks to reach the top of a ridge, and another 20 minutes of easier climbing to reach a spectacular viewpoint. The Douglas firs had burned up there, leaving bare sandstone and a clear view in all directions. I could see Bellingham far below, amazed how much altitude I'd gained. But I wasn't really sure from which angle I was seeing the city, and as I had never surveyed the territory from this vantage, none of the hills around me looked familiar.

My disorientation should have been an important hint to retrace my steps back down the switchbacks to familiar ground. My last dose of meds would be wearing off presently, and I had limited energy. When I'm off, my thinking is muddled. But I kept going, guessing that the trail would soon begin its descent towards Samish Road. And then what? Samish was well-traveled, but I didn't know if buses went out that far. Good planning. Not.

I followed a bike track downhill and came to a kiosk covered with a cedar shake roof. So far as I could tell, I was still in the middle of the woods. There was a map of the trails on the mountain, but my Parkinson's-clouded brain couldn't grasp the way out of the maze, even though a yellow pin in the map told me where I was: at a kiosk in the middle of the woods.

With Parkinson's disease there is always an hourglass whose sand is about to run out. I checked the time. I had another hour before my dose, according to my watch, so I must have been in a parkinsonian time warp; it felt like I was starting to stiffen up. I reached into my pill bottle and fingered a half-tab of 100-mg. quick-release Sinemet, which I ground with my teeth and mixed with the saliva in my mouth to speed absorption.

Hearing distant traffic but uncertain about the direction of its source, I continued my downhill journey, past a clear-cut area where I saw slash piles tall as a two-story house. After another half-mile, I came to a treeless corridor that veered away from the road, grassy slopes descending in 50-yard-long steps as far as I could see. Signposts said a natural gas pipeline was buried beneath the slope—part of the same natural gas pipeline that sent a devastating firestorm through Whatcom Falls Park a decade earlier. I decided to go that way, toward the park, I thought. After a couple miles, I came to a spur that jogged right, leading to a residential street with expensive houses. I didn't know what neighborhood it was, so I asked a resident out in his yard. He gave me directions ("That way," he said, pointing behind him with his thumb over his shoulder). I once was lost and now I'm found. It was easy to get home from there.

The fact that I ended up miles from where I thought I would end up and had gotten off track so quickly was sobering. Sustaining any injury while alone on a mountain under a gray sky threatening rain could have been a real problem. I wondered how I would have described my location to rescuers. Fortunately nothing bad happened.

Okay. Again, I wasn't Reinhold Messner soloing K2 without oxygen, nor was I Joshua Slocum, the first man to circumnavigate the globe in a single-handed sailboat, trying to survive in the Roaring Forties latitudes with half a world yet to travel. But it was my little adventure, Lost on Galbraith Mountain.

And you know what? I'm kind of proud of myself. Not

knowing where the trail you're on is going may be stupid, but never setting out at all is just as stupid. I'll keep trying to find my way as a PWP who still finds joy in just walking.

23.

Vulnerability

I don't even need to be lost in the woods to come face to face with my vulnerability.

It was ten in the morning on a sunny February weekday. I was walking along Cornwall Avenue near the high school.

"Hey you!" a voice somewhere behind me shouted. I kept walking. "Hey! You!" the voice repeated, closer now. I turned this time and came face to face with a man who had bad news written all over him, his teeth bad, facial skin swelled possibly as a result of too much beer and whiskey, or whatever. Long hair and beard. A mean-looking thug.

Another guy walked up from a different direction, came into my view with a six-foot length of heavy, skull-cracking chain, part of it wrapped around his forearm so that he could really put some force into his delivery.

"That's a weapon," I said, stating the obvious while I stared at the chain.

"Yeah," said the chain guy, "I'm going to use it on the asshole who disrespected our woman. You fit the description of the guy."

They suddenly seemed like cavemen who had escaped from an episode of *The Simpsons* carrying deadly wooden clubs, grunting, "Our women! Nnnggt! Belong to us!" and thumping chests with their fists.

I couldn't believe I was in this situation and had no idea

what they were talking about or how I ended up their prime suspect. I was fortunate enough to not only be clueless, but more importantly to convincingly appear to be clueless. They let me walk. The chain guy even said, "Sorry, man," as he put out his unchained hand and began some elaborate urban handshake that I awkwardly fumbled my way through.

That was it. Maybe five minutes. But I was uneasy for a couple of months and avoided that part of town for weeks.

A year or so later I read a story in the paper about a gang-related killing. A man was attacked by gang members in Bellingham, including a guy who apparently threatened to chain-whip the would-be victim. But the victim had a pocket knife and stabbed chain-guy once. In the heart. I wondered if it was the same chain guy I had faced and whether the poor soul was killed by someone less innocent and naive than I had been.

Parkinson's is only so large. It can only take up a finite amount space in our lives. There are meaner, more devastating forces at work in the world, many of them worse than what I face.

In fact, I feel really, really lucky.

24.

The Voice of God

Music must be the most transcendent art form. Through music we can become whole again. Emerson wrote in the 19th century, "Music takes us out of the actual and whispers to us dim secrets that startle our wonder as to who we are, and for what, whence, and whereto."

These are exactly the questions with which I have been skirmishing during my life with Parkinson's disease. There is a sense of surprise and wonder when music makes me ask, "Who I am and why am I here?"

Making music was satisfying for me during my pre-Parkinson's life and in the early years following diagnosis. Now it's just frustrating. But listening to great music played or sung by other people, live or recorded, can be transformative.

I went to a Celtic-music themed concert before Christmas 2010, knowing it would be long and would probably wear me out sitting in a crowded hall. But something magical happened. The music made me float blissfully for four hours without medication, fatigue, or any Parkinson's symptoms! There was a lot of emotional impact, because I used to play Irish music, and now I couldn't, but it didn't matter. For a few hours, purely from being elevated to a level of deep joy, I forgot I had Parkinson's.

On another night, this one 35 years ago, I sat alone in a basement apartment in Seattle with a single candle for light, and I listened to all four sides of Keith Jarrett's solo-piano Köln concert, recorded live in January of 1975. I didn't so much listen as become part of the music. It took me to another world where everything made sense. I listen to that particular Jarrett recording every few years, and every time I hear it I go back to that space where life is joy, is music.

I grew up with a musical mom and step-dad. She played keyboards, including church organ, and he was a singer and choir director. When I was 10, my mother would say proudly whenever the topic of music came up, "Ricky listens to classical music," as if this were some remarkable new accomplishment, as if I'd just become an astronaut.

"My son goes up into space," I can imagine Mom saying.

I was living proof that, if parents try long enough (I had an older brother and sister), they'll get an introspective "good" kid who complies with the authorities and acts grown up in weird ways. I was that kid.

I can't recall what classical music I listened to. Maybe once Mom saw me take an LP out of its jacket and put it on the turntable. It might have been Beethoven.

My folks were into musicals by the great composers and lyricists of the mid-twentieth century: Rodgers & Hammerstein, Lerner & Loewe, Frank Loesser, Bernstein & Sondheim, George & Ira Gershwin.

They worked all day at sales jobs and did theater at night. I can't remember them being at home much, except when they threw a party for the cast of their most recent show. Otherwise, when they were home, they were uptight and hurrying to get somewhere else.

I guess all parents work with what they've got. Some express affection more than others. Later on, in college, I shut them out, but when I was 10, boy, I was the good kid who finally arrived after two wild horses (my brother and sister) had already trampled the pasture.

There was an African-American man in my folks' circle of musicians and singers named Henry Brantly. He had a booming baritone voice. Henry was the guy my mom was talking about when she said proudly, "Some of my best friends are Negroes."

"Some"—that'd be Henry.

Henry drank too much. I probably would have gotten drunk, too, if I'd been in his shoes—a black man in a white world with white friends. I never knew of him having any black friends. Maybe he did, but if so he was very secretive about it.

He liked me. Henry taught me how to set stage lights and work the control board when preparations were in progress for a production of James Weldon Johnson's *God's Trombones,* a musical interpretation of the Creation story based on the Book of Genesis.

I still can hear Henry's voice-of-God narration with which the piece begins:

> *And God stepped out on space,*
> *And he looked around and said:*
> *I'm lonely—*
> *I'll make me a world.*

When Henry said "I'm lonely," he sounded exactly like James Earl Jones doing the voice of Darth Vader in *Star Wars.* The word *lo-o-o-o-o-n-nely* went on for about 10 seconds. Henry's thundering baritone voice was, to me, the voice of God. I can't imagine God doing a better job than Henry.

I imagine it was also Henry's very human cry for help. *I'm so lonely.*

Even though I couldn't really read music, I knew enough to nail all the lighting cues I'd written in the margins of my copy of the score.

My mom, of course, told everybody, "Ricky was the lighting technician," as if I'd just graduated from UCLA with a degree in astrophysics.

Fifty years later, I became involved in a project to highlight the benefits of dance for people with Parkinson's disease. A tortoise with Parkinson's, I stood fitfully on the dance floor at the Fairhaven Firehouse Performing Arts Center. It was mid-December. Guys moved heavy stage lights around and clamped them to metal bars near the walls and overhead. I was worried about the one directly over the spot where I stood.

Across that gulf of time, I can still see Henry Brantly teaching me the finer points of lighting design and installation for *God's Trombones.* He was the only one in the church-affiliated chorus of all white people who had any practical theater set-building and lighting skills, so with a little help from me, he did the complete setup.

Three video cameras were being positioned by the cinematographer, while my dance teacher waited in the shadows, ready to direct me in my performance for a film that was going to be entered into the American Academy of Neurology Foundation-sponsored "Neuro Film Festival."

There I stood. Under the lights. A production assistant slapped the clapper in front of me, and somebody said "Action," which I thought was a little corny. The music I had chosen to play in the studio was Henry Purcell's (1659 – 1695) *Fantasies for violas da gamba,* most of which were composed when Purcell was 21 years old.

How young the artists of the 17th century had to learn composition, painting technique, or sculpture to create a body of work that would endure beyond their relatively short lives!

The cameras began rolling. I had a space of about four feet by four feet beyond which I was not to go because I'd be out of the frame.

The first track on the Purcell CD, the *Fantasy in D Minor,* emerged from silence and darkness to an ethereal hum of bowed strings trying to find a resolution even as the piece was just getting off the ground.

I was immediately in the zone. The music carried me like a breeze carries a leaf. I used everything in my small movement vocabulary to harmonize with the music. I provided counterpoint to the viols. I expanded and contracted. I was happy. The cameras, lights, people—all disappeared for two minutes. I didn't need direction. The dance was self-creating.

Once the moment ended and we were back in "time," we worked on more proscribed pieces for another two hours. I'd had my time of bliss.

I wonder what Henry Brantly would have said. Or thought. His performance has been somewhere in my mind for all these years. He had been in that magical, private but revealing place in *God's Trombones.*

"I'm lonely. I'll make me a world."

Doesn't that sound like what we all try to do?

25.

Snow and Shadows

We've had our first snow of the winter. That was a couple days ago. Now it's cold and dry. Outside the window, even before I get out of bed, I see snowflakes blown from the roof hovering or bobbing up and down in the frigid air. They remind me of fireflies on a summer evening in the Midwest, small illuminations hanging in the languid atmosphere.

I get out of bed, bundle up, put on my boots, and go outside to walk the trail through the park.

On the trail, snow weighs down the tree branches which I have to duck under as I pass. Occasionally, I stop and shake the powdery snow off a Douglas fir bough, fascinated by how the limb lightens and rises back up to its unburdened position. So it is with overcoming burdens of any sort. Removing the weight of depression in my forties allowed me to become my real self again, not something that was not already part of my deeper nature and identity. Treating depression is like shaking the snow loose. I go back to an original, higher functioning level of being.

But the pristine snow is accompanied by my low mood, my shadow self wanting attention. Not enough Vitamin D.

I have fears, lots of them. For the most part I keep them at bay. I realize that writing this book has brought them, the fears, to the surface, dripping with the lagoon water from which they have emerged. Out where I have to look at them, one by one, as I feel them caressing me with their cold wet hands.

I am afraid that everyone I love will disappear.

I am afraid of being abandoned.

I am afraid I will disappear.

I am afraid of being helpless.

I am afraid I will simply vanish into dementia.

What keeps me going? I don't have any special inspiration, no extraordinary grit. I haven't become a Buddhist. I have no heroic deeds to perform. I just need to keep trying to do whatever it is I do, and to smile more.

Whenever I am outside the city and the night sky is clear, all I have to do is look up at the stars and, corny as it sounds, I enter a state of wonder. How could death be an ending, when we are a part of all that, part of the cosmos? When I started writing these essays a few months ago, I failed to see the mystery. The stars now glimmer with questions.

Anything I need to know is light years away, ancient beyond imagining but traveling in my direction.

The tortoise with Parkinson's disease dances, but there is no audience to watch my slow, elegant performance. Isn't that the way it goes? Just because I'm ready to show myself, with my limitations, my fears and anger, my depression, what remains of my soul, it doesn't mean that the world is interested in my process at this particular moment.

Years ago, Lee and I agreed to consciously choose quality of life in the near term—meaning we would not postpone taking the most current medical treatments available for our chronic illnesses, treatments that relieve symptoms but are not without risks and possible long-term damage. We chose to live in the present. In my case,

I started out on Sinemet, which, 14 years later, continues to work very well. My neurologist added a dopamine agonist later. Other neurologists postpone treating young-onset Parkinson's disease (YOPD) with carbidopa-levodopa because they apparently feel that patients may really need it later on, and by starting too soon they may deveop early problems with dyskinesias, or might use up the drug's effectiveness, which can have a diminishing therapeutic value over time. Starting on a regimen of a dopamine agonist, for example, instead of carbidopa-levodopa, is a decision that the neurologist should make in conjunction witn an informed patient. There may really be no right answer. The medications for Parkinson's disease affect different people in different ways. But when I talk to newly diagnosed Parkinson's patients, I am sometimes surprised at how little information is given to them about medical options.

That, in part, is why finding a medical center that employs movement disorder specialists is important in getting treatment started on the right track, with options laid out, allowing the patient to be part of the decision-making process regarding his or her treatment.

I believe I would make the same treatment decision again, given the opportunity. But I don't have an "again." All I can work with is "now."

Had Lee and I made a deal with the universe? Is this the "later" that we have traded away for near-term quality of life?

It's not that I think I'll die today, or even this year. But I admit to feeling older than I "should." There are still doorways to a meaningful life.

And I will find those doors and open them, one by one.

Epilogue: The Mythology of Illness

Because Parkinson's disease has dogged my every step for the past 20 years, done its best to undermine my thinking process, deconstructed my identity, and left me exhausted and isolated, vulnerable to the slightest ill wind that blows my way, I had to write about it. I have been forced to make adjustments. I make space for PD in my life because I must. I would not make a coffee date with PD at Starbucks so that we could talk. PD dawdles along beside me anyway. But when I write about it, I feel strangely distant from the disease itself.

I've written to some degree about how I cope with the PD, which has changed my life and taught me enough to satisfy my curiosity about neurological illness for several lifetimes. These stories are the only stories that I could write. For now, the inspiration and energetic forces that visited me have simply evaporated. I certainly haven't exhausted the topic, but that's all there is to say. For now.

So let the members of the cast go back to wherever they came from—the island, the tortoise, the lagoon and reef, the sea. Let's get on with life; isn't that what we do? Get on with life, indeed. Soldier on. Stiff upper lip. When the going gets tough. God never gives you anything you're not ready to handle. All those brave words that I want to believe in. The suggestion that I am not fully alive, that I have been cut down to size by Parkinson's, does not resonate with the meager portion of hope that pulls me along like a hooked fish.

A precarious balance exists between my optimism and my despair. My low mood may keep me from seeing things as they really are. But this is how things really are. If I deny my shadow aspect, a concept taken from Jungian psychology, I create my own myth about Parkinson's disease. Illness is real, that's for sure. But illness may not be what we think it is.

For example, I once believed that there is something out there in the universe called "Parkinson's disease," which has an existence of its own. One "gets" it, or one "has" it. Thus, I also believe that the statement "I have Parkinson's disease" is true. The way I use language reflects my beliefs about what constitutes reality. At the end of the day I have PD, no bones about it.

I think Parkinson's disease can be better characterized as a process, a discontinuity of healthy functioning, that involves as-yet undiscovered causes. It's a noncommunicable disease, supposedly, but how can we say even that if the cause is unknown? Is it just as reasonable for me to say that "Parkinson's dreams about me" as it is to say "I have Parkinson's disease?"

In 1978, essayist, critic, and novelist Susan Sontag wrote an extremely influential book, *Illness as Metaphor,* when she was battling cancer. In the book she argued against the thinking then current: that diseases were associated with personal psychological traits. She exposed the mythology of illness that was evident in our culture at the time during which she was sick. She went after the belief that people with cancer (or, earlier, tuberculosis) were somehow responsible for their illnesses because of their character. Cancer was, in that view, an expression of things one was trying to repress.

In Sontag's own words, "The romantic idea that the disease expresses the character is invariably extended to assert that the character causes the disease, because it has not expressed itself."

So, in a sense, the person with cancer is to blame for allowing cancer to develop.

The mythology of illness comprises our unexamined beliefs about the nature of the relationship between the illness and the ill. But blaming the patient for manifesting the disease cuts both ways and can lead to a kind of magical thinking that one can self-heal from cancer, Parkinson's, MS, or ALS without the intervention of modern or any kind of medicine except one's own inner resources. If spontaneous healing occurs, then it is truly miraculous.

The Australian John Coleman claims self-healing from Parkinson's disease, and I don't disbelieve him. But my belief or disbelief is really beside the point. What matters is what really occurred, and I will probably never know. I'm not going to take his word for it based on what he writes in a book. As I have demonstrated, there are no regulations specifying who can or cannot write and publish a book. I would, to be honest, probably not try employing Coleman's methodology—I'm not sure I have the energy.

We take illness so personally ("why me?") and yet treat it as something completely outside ourselves, a nuisance or threat to be gotten rid of. We should not take the blame for our illnesses, but at the same time we should take responsibility for trying to live a good and meaningful life despite our disease. We are not the disease, nor did we cause it to attack our brain cells.

What is heartening, for me, is that there is room for modern medicine, belief in God, positive thinking, and the power of self-healing to form an integrative approach that is ultimately pragmatic. If something helps, use it. Don't be the man stranded in the ocean who keeps rejecting things that could help him survive, but holds fast to his belief that God will save him, when it is, in fact, God who has provided the raft, the helicopter, and other means of rescue. The man rejects all these because of misunderstanding the nature of God's help.

But back to Parkinson's disease, and living with it. This part of the book is over. I have tried to describe what the monster looks like to me. My stories are diversions that may or may not connect to truth. If you "have" Parkinson's disease, as I do, recognize that I have tried not to pretend I have any answers, even though it is difficult to write a book without believing you have something to say.

My own experience living with Parkinson's disease at times seems like a losing battle. Although I considered subtitling the book *My Life with Parkinson's Disease,* PD has really only constituted one third of my life. But some days it seems I've been living with it forever. I grow depressed.

Then one morning I wake up and it doesn't feel so bad, so complicated, so hopeless. I feel the stirrings of possibility, I take a deep breath, and I try again (and again) to lead the life I've been given.

PART THREE

Selected Poems

photo by Lee Willis

Very seldom do I feel normal. This poem starts off lamenting the fact that I am not the right size to blend into the crowd, then it goes on, with some irony, to embrace the middle way, the path of Mother Bear.

The Right Size

If I could be just the right size,
life would be much easier.
I could buy pants that matched
my waist size and inseam length.
I could walk through a doorway
without ducking, and if I bought a
new bike, I wouldn't have to
special order an extra-large frame.

If I came in a modified,
more compact configuration,
I could attempt new positions
and adopt conventional strategies.
I am just on the cusp of normal,
my moon is waning and waxing,
never settling down in a nice place
like Aries or Libra.

Definitely I would no longer slouch.
My backbone would be stronger,
my resolve more resolute,
and I would have just the right amounts
of time and money with which to do
the expected things: comb my hair,
call my brother, walk three miles,
drink two beers, and worry just enough.

If I could be just the right size,
I could write the appropriate words
in precisely the correct order
to attract a literate, loyal audience.

If I could find the perfect size envelope,
I would send this poem off
to a post office box somewhere
in a midwestern swing state
during an off-year election.
The average person
could easily understand it
and vote for normalization
of the nation's foreign policy.

If I could be Mama Bear's soup,
that would suit me fine.
My favorite word is *tepid*.
I don't boil closer to sea level.
I've crossed the Tropic of Capricorn
at sea only once, when the wind
was blowing lightly in the right direction.

In a way, this is the most positive poem in this small collection. Although it is something of a romp, the central premise of reincarnation allows me to indirectly express those qualities and capabilities that I seem to lack in this life, which as far as I can tell is the only one I have.

If I Come Back

If I am actually reincarnated,
I want to come back as a glass half full,
a partly sunny day,
with the benefit of the doubt.
I want to come back as the long shot,
the sweet spot,
beaming affirmation,
not impossibly happy
but knowing how to get there.

Soon enough
I'll be a child again.
I'll be thirty-something
once more.
I'll take early retirement
and leave buckets of money
to the right people.

If I come back,
if I am actually reincarnated,
I want to be a 16th-century
lute maker
or a deep monk
in a snowy Transylvanian monastery
praying and chanting all night.

If I am reincarnated,
reborn for the umpteenth time,
I want to be someone
with talent to burn,
but flying below the radar
in the Middle Ages
of the middle-aged.

If I am reincarnated,
really, I want to come back
as someone
filled with unconditional love
for all sentient beings
and to know that
I will face the
blinding brightness:
annealing,
oxidizing, burning,
purified.

That's how I want to go out.

If I breathe again after taking
my last breath,
if I am hatched,
calved, cloned, thrown,
dropped, or whelped,
I want it to be into a better world
than the one I live in now,
but also one as rich
with choices and consequences.

A glass half full:
that's what I'll be,
if I come back.

At the end of a particularly difficult week during which I struggled with the effects of my medications wearing off early, experienced deeper and longer off periods and tried to put the brakes on downward-spiraling depression, I wrote the following poem. Perhaps not the best of circumstances under which to write anything at all.

The Time of My Life

What can I possibly be waiting for?
The hard times, the soft moans,
the years of work—
all that is behind me.

I am still productive,
but for different reasons.
Now I get paid a living wage
for simply breathing.
I receive thank-yous from groups
of faithful strangers,
to whom I am also a stranger.

My words begin to quiet themselves
like elk under the prairie stars,
their breathing presence
defined by shadows.

Yesterday, I couldn't move my legs.
Turning slowly into stone, I will know
when it is too late to do
what I have dreamed of doing.

Shifting sails with the wind's breath,
I can make a poor voyage
to the opposite shore, on a good day.
But sometimes, just breathing is not enough.
I'd like to love people more than a little,
before the time of my life
is no longer mine to live,
when the silent elk breathlessly
rise into the sky above me,
until they, too,
become the ancient light of stars.

I saw three geese on Derby Pond, and the first stanza came to me as walked the rest of the way home. I quickly wrote it down and it took off from there. A lighthearted lampoon, there's also something in it about accepting who you are.

An Ode to Geese

O dull-headed gander, goose, and gosling:
your honking—melodious as the
digital salsa ringtone
from the cell phone of a man sitting next to you
on an overbooked flight to Sacramento—
when will *you* fly home?

Every bleeding heart and crimson azalea
in the woodland surrounding you
lifts its blossoms skyward, in radiant silence.
Can't the three of you, or the three thousand of you,
bleat at least the same note,
up or down an octave, or harmonizing in fifths,
when you pass over my house?

It has something to do with the way you muck about
for your escargot and scum-bearded pond weeds,
nothing like the kingfisher's patient,
laser-beam attack
from the dead branch of a snag
onto a wild trout's boney spine in clear water.

But, okay, you are not kingfishers.
Still, there are things I like about you.
I like the flying V-formation, very cool,
very more-than or less-than,
maybe a herald of some distant victory,
or the inverted direction to heaven.

Also, I like the spontaneous takeoffs
from muddy Skagit River delta land,
where you've been eating fertile alluvial dirt
since time began.
Motionless as cabbages,
you doze until, suddenly,

Boom!

Thousands of you shift your shoulders back and up,
engaging wings, all at once and as with one mind,
with one instinctual whoosh,
your crap oozing down onto the fields, roads, and cars
instantly far beneath you, you rise
as though the earth has repelled you.

And then, wheeling high above the fields,
you vocalize your longing to be what you are not,
letting go chaotic, choking sound pulses,
the monstrous honking of a thousand coal trains,
a mournful cacophony of dissonant,
sharply inflected song, so out of touch
with this world's lavishly honed beauty
and practiced cheerfulness.

You will never be eagles.
Just geese: bullying, dumpy,
fat-assed geese. But honk for what you are,
and I will honk in return. I will put a
"Honk if you heart geese"
bumper sticker on the back of my Prius.
Brothers and sisters, honk your uniqueness
to the skies, and stand your fouled ground.

Published in the chapbook of poems accepted for Phrasings 2012, *an annual performance collaboration between dancers and poets. This poem was interpreted and choreographed by Angela Kiser and performed with Ian Bivins on April 29, 2012, at the Firehouse Performing Arts Center in Bellingham, Washington.*

Breathwork

the active
creative motion
undergoes change
in substance
weight
tending back toward
the passive
ethereal
light
wind
and belief
self and shadow
intercourse
one another
creating active balance
harmonized returning
motion

the wind
imprints
the landscape
undulations in grass
leaves
clouds
spirit dances
on in-breath
let the work
consume
you

Letting Go of All That

I wake to dreaming,
walk through the oldest part of the forest,
see everything
close up.

The river leaps, my heart beating—
my heart,
still heavy with desire.

If I could have a sign—
a broken twig, a scrap of paper,
crumbs from your coat pocket—
maybe I could find you,
if you want to be found.

Was that love, walking
into the forest, following no path,
seduced into the deepest groves,
never to be heard from again?

Ashes from the fire that once burned:
when did it happen?
You say my memory is going.
My morning lust
no longer hot.

Our bodies have become shopworn,
our bones hangers for spent flesh.
We once made eye contact,
consecrating our vows to follow
the cycle of time.

We've planted the seed.
Now it is time
to let go of all that.
I stop counting years
and naming each winter day.
Finding the slippery trail
is not difficult.
Oregon grape leaves drip rain.
Stone on stone creates hard communion.
Following the frozen stream.
Finding sleep.

This happens more than once.

The images of dislocation, physical deformity, and a call for help inform this recent poem with a surrealistic, disjointed atmosphere, within which I can't help but see and hear references to the symptoms of Parkinson's disease, even though that's not what I set out to express.

Billy the Kid's Last Ride

The Kid, his head kiltered to one side,
sat the wheelchair like it was a king's throne.
He said to me,

When does the next bus come by here?

We were on a river somewhere,
in Wyoming maybe,
and it was Joo-ly the fourth,
some years past.

That boy is a calamity

purred the coffee-gossip ladies
from town.
True, he was upon some hard times.

Kept saying
When does the next bus come by here?
I been waiting and waiting.

Calamity Jane his mom.
Legs like two gun barrels
that could shoot sparks,
if the mood suited.
I said to him,
"I've seen you running to catch my bus."

The Kid's head leaned harder,
near-parallel with the rust-red dirt
below our feet. Both knowing
that was not possible.

What time's the bus come by today?
he repeated.

We were on the edge of a canyon.
I focused on small nearby things
such as the spider
on the scrub juniper berry.
The Kid sat his wheelchair like it was
a Warmblood mare,
tipped his broad-brimmed hat.

You don't think those ladies'll shoot me, do you?

My legs began to stiffen,
in condolence, I suppose.
My arms, then my fingers,
chest, heart.
I tilted my head to one side,
sat down in my wheelchair.
It was like sitting a buggy seat
in the 1870s. Somewhere,
Wyoming maybe.

Once more, his kid-like, reedy voice—

When does the next bus come by here?
I been waiting and waiting.

My relationship with a woman I once loved did not survive a coast-to-coast roundtrip car journey in a 1964 Dodge Dart. On our way back from New York to Seattle, we wandered through the parks of British Columbia and Alberta, finally crossing the border into Washington State. We both knew this trip was the beginning of the end for us, and we saw each other in a different, less favorable light after spending four weeks together in a car. The poem was first drafted in 1974, revised and completed in 2012.

Crossing the Border

Morning
From the country west of Edmonton,
last light,
the smells of bread and campfire smoke
inside the car all night.
Sleeping over at Wild Horse Lake,
having seen bear, coyote
and heard birds calling across the water;
three Albertan fishermen had given us their report,
one trout that gleamed from the fire
as they walked past our camp,
hanging at one man's side like a knife
before they climbed into the pickup
and disappeared back towards the Jasper highway.
We ate soup and rice,
finishing together as the wind rose, then
burrowing all night out of it inside the sleeping bags,
making love as the wind shushed our moans,
then my head just above the food box:
honey, bread, and our salts and spices for
cooking in the alder-wood fires;

smoke in my clothes and hair,
the scent my bone grey sweater
has absorbed after nights of bending down
to blow on coals and make the flames
lick up into the bottom of the
blue metal pots holding soup
that ashes drift into
like quiet thoughts from the lake we rise to watch,
now that it's morning.

Gathering
just dry sticks for the fire, north of Peyto Lake,
then Yoho; along a river
branches snap and the bear looks up.
Water walks behind me,
over stones and old campsites.
The bear's claws pry at the darkened window,
my mouth goes dry as the stale bread he smells,
the bread that I made in Seattle, and ate,
that he wants to devour, and I want
to trade him for the thin blue cloth
of the tent we lie beneath / that I breathe under,
hearing his claws at the windshield
seeing an eye reflected in the rear view mirror
that I look through / seeing morning / where he
crushes a branch of the rose-hips
and tugs loose the handle on the camp water pump
and crosses the river, grumbling
his hump back among his rocks and trees.
You do not need any protecting.
I never really understood you.

Washington

South and west across the border,
still north of Omak,
in dry-mouth country. In the shimmering heat
of America, I see you taking a different road.
None of this is spoken.
Driving past old homesteads still standing,
ribs of weather darkened Ponderosa pines
growing in hot-rock canyons, we wonder
if the bald front tire will get us back to Seattle.
The road is straighter here after the mountains,
the wood drier for burning in fires along the coast.
The ranches still going
holed in dry scrub hollows well back from any road.
A distant line of cottonwoods
marks the path of the Okanogan River
that flows by the town
where Little Ron was born Colville
and called the white lady Grandmother.

Frog painting by Amanda Murray. Photo by Lee Willis.

My adopted younger brother is a chartered member of the Upper Nicola band near Merritt, B.C. The Upper Nicola are a part of the Okanagan Nation. His wife, my sister-in-law, is Tsimshian, the People of the Skeena River in northern British Columbia. Many Tsimshian chiefs' rattles feature a man whose tongue is joined to that of a frog, representing the sharing of power between the People and their spirit guides.

Frog Outwits the Youthful Drummer

The first time,
Frog's escape from his painted image
on the drum surprises me.
He jumps straight out
of the skin drumhead, heart beating,
chest billowing and caving
with life.

He leaps towards me,
lands on my shoulder
close to my neck,
breathing and shimmering wet.

The elders sit around the fire,
calmly watching.
This ceremony
tests my power,
showing that I no longer
live as a child.
I hold the drum stick, really ready
to pound away, make lots of impressive noise,
make my manhood ring loud and clear.

But Frog, licking my skin
with his sweetest poison,
makes me forget who I am,

gets me laughing
so hard that he escapes
before I can chase him back into the drum.

When I finally hit the taut skin
with the wooden-handled stick
carved like a Raven's head,
my senses are so numb
that I can barely hear
the deep thrum of the drums
or the high voices of the singers.

Hundreds of frogs
fall from the sky
like rain.
The seated elders act
as if this situation was normal.

From when I was a boy,
I remember learning that
the chrysalis holds the butterfly,
tadpole becomes frog.
Everything transforming.
One world becomes the past,
the gravesite of ancestors,
the source of wisdom,
stories passed on since
the beginning of time.
That's the dead familiar world
sloughing its skin with a shrug.

Old grandmother
sitting near the fire
laughs
as again I strike the drum
with my stick.
The elders smile patiently
at my fumbling inexperience.

"Do you think all those frogs
falling from the sky
are the People who have died,
now coming back to earth
as toads?" Grandmother asks me,
cackling her way
out to the woods, squatting
in the shadows
to pee. "I hope you know more about girls
than you know about frogs," she yells
from behind her veil of bushes.

I had forgotten all about Frog.
How hard can it be to keep a frog
inside a drum? His face is painted
right there, and yet I didn't know
that Frog's song was my own.
I'll sing it to that
pretty girl in Fairbanks.

My wife and I have been traveling to a special place on Vancouver Island for several years to celebrate our anniversary in early October. During one of those stays in a cabin by the Salish Sea, I wandered along rocky points and coves, finally finding a crude wooden bench near the shore where I sat down. The wind was up and I was looking south in the direction of its reach. A heron flew past, I dug my notebook out of my bag, turned to an open page and the words started to appear, as if I was taking dictation. The next autumn, I received the second and third poems from the same spot. But the following year the voice was gone. I think maybe it was because I got greedy and took two poems in one year.

Three Visions / Vancouver Island

1. How I Got Here

The first deer wander down by my place
to eat windfall apples in the old orchard.
I planted those apple trees,
way back when. I've lived here a long time.

Once we tried to cut down all the red cedar.
There were all these spirits at my back:
they hid in the woods or out in the water.
Orca, coyote, raven.
Even the stones had spirits,
some good,
some bad.
Just like people.

Some of those old trees survived, and
they became my ancestors.
Back then oysters clogged the shoreline.
Their shells became this white-sand beach.

We told lots of jokes
about things that could harm us,
like the jealous husband who died
and came back as a mosquito.
After that, we laughed whenever we slapped
    mosquitos.

I dreamed I was flying over the water,
could see the great Tahoma,
way off.
Hit the water, went under,
and became a salmon.
I could see clear to where I was born,
up a shallow creek off the Nooksack.
That's the spot where I'll die.

When people came,
the madrona trees arched high above their greasy
    camps.
After that things were really different.

The voices that tell people
to do good in the world
are hidden deep in thick tree-bark.
The deer are struggling from their graves,
for this is a time of little food.

Just before I leave here,
Heron flies by. He says,
"You'd better not tell anyone this story."

That's all he said.

2. Man Who Takes Trees

I sit against the trunk of an old cedar,
just looking out at the smoke rising
from a distant fire somewhere to the south.
Below me, on the rocks near the salt water,
Man Who Takes Trees is doing something strange.
He is drinking salt water, then gagging
and spitting it back up.

He keeps doing that until I finally can't stand it any
    more.
"Takes Trees!" I call. "Why are you trying to drink
    salt water?"
He looks up at me, eyes gleaming, yells back,
"Look, the tide is really way out there.
I want to be ready if it doesn't come back in.
I am practicing salmon breathing."

Takes Trees goes back to his drinking and vomiting.
Children are frightened of his strange, mossy
    appearance.
They walk quickly along the forest path
with baskets full of ripe berries.
They look over their shoulders
to see whether Man Who Takes Trees is quietly
    following them,
would like to take *them*.
They find the stones he has piled, one on another.
They look like stone totem poles,
but these spirits have lost their ancestral faces.

When he drinks salt water,
because the tide may never flow again,
because all the streams may run dry,

I think Man Who Takes Trees is no fool.
Once he told me that if this Place goes dry,
the Whole Great Creation is done for.

3. Talking to Spirits

The island across all that water we call Otter's Back.
We name all the clouds, too, each cloud a different
     name.
Seabirds in large groups soar and squawk,
feeding in the rich chaos of the sea currents.

When I was growing up, school made me feel like I
     was drowning.
I daydreamed, named clouds, like the one who
looked like my uncle, twisted and humped
with palsy—I named that cloud Water Goes Slow.

Started drinking hard liquor in junior high. Years
     later
I came back to the Place, to come into my power.
Then all that bad stuff stopped. But it took some
     effort.

When the sky turns gray, like the weathered,
barkless trees tossed to the top of the tide line,
I become like a mountain, strong in my heart.
I been tryin' to find stories in the driftwood, maybe
have a vision.

Now I am old, but I still feel my oats.
I've been on airplanes. We never believed
that they were birds or other such nonsense.
We figured they'd make a good way to get
over to Otter's Back.

I remember a time in my youth when my brothers
    paddled by
as I stood on the rocky shore. I heard drums all
    around me,
talking to spirits: All this had been created:
rocks, salmon, water, clouds, red cedar,
what we need to live.
All this was here.
I know where the sun is going to rise.
How can people know that and still lose
their way?

I wrote this poem in 1973 and dedicated it to my brother Ron, who has made adventure and solitude in the wilderness a major component of his life. This predates the Parkinson's disease I live with now. I want to include it to honor my brother, who suffered near-fatal injuries in a plane crash around the time this was written.

Edward Hopper Goes Fraser River Canyon

Nothing but volumes of light
and emptiness
in a rundown storefront,
circa 1930.

A facade of faded red walls,
silent bricks, a shaft of light—
I could stare forever
at that Hopper print.

Keeping vigil in another county of my wall,
a U.S. roadmap, strip
of southern Canada.
The Fraser River scars a corner

of British Columbia,
pouring southwest of a thumbtack
and into my room.
I see my brother

in his green kayak
moving inside the whiteness
of the river,
slipping between jagged sawteeth

of snow and ice.
He moves alone,
the sky opening like a hand above him.
Birds hang motionless

in the canyon air,
paralyzed with light.
They watch the one living thing
below, in his country of silence,

the solitude I feel today
in this room full of white doors
I open one by one,
listening for any trickle.

An old Mississippi Delta bluesman once said that you need to feel good to play the blues. When you've got the blues, you don't feel like playin' nothin'.

When I Get What I Call the Blues

When I get what I call the blues,
I don't care what anybody thinks.
Man, you can beat that drum
all day long, and I don't hear a thing.

When I get what I call the blues,
I start driving up roads to places
I know I don't want to be.
Robert Johnson could be at the crossroads
singing "Kind-Hearted Woman"
and I wouldn't notice.

When I get what I call the blues,
none of the people on this bus
have souls. Me either.
If Blind Lemon Jefferson
sat himself down in this chair
I wouldn't recognize him,
but I'd take his guitar.

When I get what I call the blues,
I can't stand listening to the blues.
You can bend that note until the string breaks,
my brother,
but it's no skin off my back.

When I get what I call the blues,
even if B.B. King taught me a special run
or some other fancy lick,
I'd be turned to dust and blown
to the next state by the time I touched
the strings of his guitar.

Beautifully

Some people say
it's never too late
to start.
Others, sighing, mutter,
it's always too late.

Then there are all the people
who put microphones
in the clouds.
They are the ones
who photocopy their faces
to prove
they are even
there.

I could've painted birds,
or raced electric cars.
I could've been a face
you've seen but the name
escapes
you.

I could've done everything
beautifully.

The type for this poem was handset in 1974 at Copper Canyon Press, Port Townsend, Washington. I've long since forgotten the name of the typeface.

the fisherman

Bait the hook
with pieces of finger.
Walk to a large river in the desert
and listen.

The river
climbs its sandstone canyon,
a black ant scrabbling
from a glass jar.

Soon there will be nothing but water.
Dead fish ripen
on the slopes of the mountain.

With your good hand
you climb once more.

prairie skin

elk grazing
in tall grass
while we
make love
gentle rain
falling
in this dream

I like crows, even though my regard for our clever and sometimes intimidating avian friends may not be evident from this poem. The refrain about "tiny feet" being the only remains of their scavenging a road-kill squirrel comes from the way my wife's cat Hieronymus used to eat mice—eating every part except the feet and nose, which would remain on the floor in situ, as if still attached to a body.

Gothic Crow #3

The angular talk of crows
is full of little lies. Given what I know
they know, dark secrets only I can hear,
It might be wise to let them go
for maybe just another year.

They often land at dinner time
near dead things in the street.
I think they think themselves quite pretty;
they never shrink or sound retreat,
even as they tear and rip
their sinewed trash with little pity.

And when they're finished eating
all the squirrel's pathetic meat,
nothing's left but tiny feet!
All that's left are tiny feet!

Bossy blackened daylight dwellers,
clinging to the highest wires,
they are, I notice, gone by night.
I almost miss their cagey, murderous
delight in picking only the best blue eggs
from the robin's nest.

Then all innocence 'til their eyes awake
at dawn, and in their clear, demented flight,
They know what's wrong!
They know what's wrong!

Glossary

This is not intended to be a comprehensive technical vocabulary. I tried to include words that I use in the book. There are a great number of sources containing many other terms related to parkinsonism.

In compiling this glossary of Parkinson's-related terminology, I used several online sources, primarily www.miriam-webster.com. I have also rephrased some of the definitions in J. Eric Ahlskog's useful and comprehensive *Parkinson's Disease Treatment Book: Partnering with Your Doctor to Get the Most from Your Medications* (Oxford University Press, 2005).

The definitions of many terms are mine alone. I am responsible for any inaccuracies and errors the reader might find herein.

bradykinesia   Extreme slowness of movements and reflexes.

carbidopa   A drug that is combined with levodopa to reduce its side-effects.

cardinal symptoms   The three (or four) main symptoms of PD: bradykinesia, resting tremor, and rigidity. Opinion differs on the inclusion of postural instability on the list, since it is common to other neurological conditions—and thus is itself not a defining symptom for Parkinson's.

cogwheel rigidity   PD symptom in which an arm or
leg "catches" during movement. Neurologists can
easily test whether this symptom is present by
holding the limb and bending and unbending it.

deep brain stimulation   DBS is a surgical treatment
involving the implantation of a medical device that
works as a brain pacemaker by sending electrical
impulses to specific parts of the brain. The FDA
approved DBS for Parkinson's disease in 2002.

delusion   Belief in something with no basis in reality.

depression   Severe despondency and dejection,
accompanied by feelings of hopelessness and
inadequacy.

dopamine agonist   Drug that exerts its
pharmacological effects by directly activating
dopamine agonist receptors. Significant
psychological and cognitive side-effects are not
uncommon.

dyskinesia   Abnormality or impairment of voluntary
movement.

executive functions   Complex cognitive processing
requiring the coordination of several subprocesses
to achieve a particular goal, which is intimately
connected with the intact function of the frontal
cortices.

freezing of gait (FOG)   Typically a transient episode,
lasting less than a minute, in which gait is halted
and the patient complains that his feet are glued
to the ground. When the patient overcomes
the block, walking can be performed relatively
smoothly.

Hoehn and Yahr Scale   Commonly used system for describing how the symptoms of Parkinson's disease progress, originally published in 1967 in the journal *Neurology* by Melvin Yahr and Margaret Hoehn.

levodopa   The amino acid that is the precursor to dopamine. Levodopa, or L-dopa, is absorbed through the digestive tract into the bloodstream and is able to cross the blood-brain barrier.

magnetic resonance imaging (MRI)   A technique that creates 3-dimensional images of body structures using strong magnetic fields.

micrographia   PD symptom in which the affected individual's handwriting becomes small and illegible due to due to decreasing control over hand muscles.

movement disorder specialist   A neurologist who has taken additional training in the subspecialty of neurology called movement disorders (as compared to other subspecialties in neurology).

multiple-system atrophy (MSA)   Parkinson's-like syndrome in which degeneration in diverse brain regions leads to problems in the control of movement, balance, blood pressure, and sexual and urinary tract function. Does not respond to standard Parkinson's medications.

neurologist   Physician specializing in diseases of the brain and nervous system.

off   The state when L-dopa is not working.

on   The state when L-dopa is working and Parkinson's symptom are relieved.

ontological argument　A philosophical argument for the existence of God that typically starts with the definition of God and concludes with His necessary existence, using a priori reasoning rather than empirical observation.

pallidotomy　A surgical operation performed on the globus pallidus that destroys brain tissue in one area in the brain that affects movement. Pallidotomies are no longer routinely used. Nondestructive procedures, especially DBS surgery, have replaced pallidotomy as the first option for surgical intervention in the treatment of Parkinson's disease.

parkinsonism　Any of several neurological conditions that resemble Parkinson's disease and that result from a deficiency or blockage of dopamine caused by neuro-degenerative disease, drugs, toxins, or injury to the brain.

PD　Parkinson's disease.

PWP　Person with Parkinson's disease.

postural instability　Lack of balance when standing or changing position. Once considered a cardinal symptoms of PD.

progressive supranuclear palsy　A rare brain disorder that causes serious and progressive problems with control of gait and balance, along with complex eye movement and thinking problems.

RA　Rheumatoid arthritis, an auto-immune disorder characterized by joint pain, stiffness, and fatigue.

rasagiline (Azilect)   An inhibitor of monoamine oxidase used as a monotherapy early in the course of Parkinson's disease.

rigidity   Stiffness or tightness of the muscles. One of the cardinal symptoms of PD.

ropinerole   A dopamine agonist. The generic name for Requip.

selective serotonin re-uptake inhibitors (SSRIs)   Class of compounds typically used as antidepressants in the treatment of depression, anxiety disorders, and some personality disorders.

silent lacunar infarct (SLI)   One type of silent stroke which usually shows no identifiable outward symptoms. Individuals who suffer an SLI are often completely unaware they have suffered a stroke. It can affect various aspects of a person's mood, personality, and cognitive functioning.

Sinemet   Brand name for the combination of carbidopa and levodopa that is used to treat the symptoms of Parkinson's disease; patented by Merck in 1962, and still the gold standard for treating PD.

substantia nigra   Portion of the brain with darkly pigmented cells that is a principal location affected by PD.

subthalamic nucleus   An area of the brain located below the thalamus and considered to play a key role in the pathophysiological origin of the parkinsonian state. One of the primary target areas for DBS surgery.

TIA   Transient ischemic attack, often described as a mini-stroke.

tremor   Involuntary trembling, usually of the hands or head. Resting tremor, as opposed to intentional tremor, is a cardinal symptom of Parkinson's disease.

vascular parkinsonism   A form of "atypical parkinsonism" in which parkinsonian symptoms (slow movements, tremor, postural instability, stiffness, and rigidity) are produced by one or more small strokes.

wearing off   A condition in which medications for PD slowly become less effective over time. Also refers to off time experienced between doses of medication.

young-onset Parkinson's disease   Receiving a Parkinson's disease diagnosis relatively early in a normal lifespan. Several watershed ages have been put forth, and there remains disagreement about a specific cut-off point. I was diagnosed at age 41 and am considered young onset.

Suggested Reading List

Ahlskog, J. Eric, *The Parkinson's Disease Treatment Book: Partnering with Your Doctor to Get the Most from Your Medications,* Oxford University Press, 2005.

In my opinion, this is the best and most comprehensive book available for general information about PD as well as in-depth discussion of how to work with your neurologist to optimize the efficacy of prescription medications. Well indexed and very readable. If I had to choose one book to have about Parkinson's this would be the one, as long as updated editions are published with current information.

Blake-Krebs, Barbara, Linda Herman, and Susan Reese, *When Parkinson's Strikes Early: Voices, Choices, Resources, and Treatment,* Hunter House Inc., Publishers, Alameda, Calif., 2001.

This guidebook and forum (which was originally an e-mail discussion group) covers symptoms, side-effects of medication, support networks, and surgery options, and explores the physical, emotional, and social struggles that face primarily young people with Parkinson's. Resources, advocacy ideas, and an index are also included. If you want to hear directly from young-onset PWPs, this is where you'll find their voices.

Coleman, John C., *Stop Parkin' and Start Livin': Reversing the Symptoms of Parkinson's Disease,* Michelle Anderson Publishing Pty Ltd, Australia, 2005.

Since I devote a significant part of Chapter 21 ("Self-Healing?") to Coleman, I won't say much more about his book here. It's available on Kindle for quite a bit less than the paperback.

Fox, Michael J., *Lucky Man,* Hyperion Books, 2003.

MJF has, of course, become the very image of young-onset PD, and the MJF Foundation is doing important research in trying to discover a cause, and a cure, for Parkinson's disease. This memoir describes Fox's life before and shortly after diagnosis. He was a mess, but tells his story without flinching.

Friedman, Joseph H., *Making the Connection between Brain and Behavior: Coping with Parkinson's Disease,* Demos Medical Publishing, LLC, 2008.

One of the things that I believe could improve patient care for PWPs is if neurologists and psychiatrists would talk to each other more frequently. Friedman, a neuroscientist, makes a move in that direction. By writing only about the non-motor symptoms of Parkinson's disease, he connects PD with issues such as fatigue, apathy, depression, anxiety, dementia, hallucinations, compulsive behavior, and other disorders that could be considered psychiatric. If you've got Parkinson's disease, with motor impairment and any of the non-motor conditions just listed, you should read this book.

Kondracke, Morton, *Saving Milly: Love, Politics, and Parkinson's Disease,* The Ballantine Publishing Group, 2001.

With a foreword by Michael J. Fox, no less. Many have read or seen the film version of this heartbreaking story. When I watched it on TV, the actors were convincingly parkinsonian, but Milly's fast decline and descent into Hell reads more like a Parkinson's-plus syndrome: multiple system atrophy, progressive supranuclear palsy, or something equally devastating. But that's beside the point. See it.

Langston, J. William and Jon Palfreman, *The Case of the Frozen Addicts,* Pantheon Books, 1995.

"In 1982, hospitals in the San Francisco Bay area were suddenly confronted with *frozen* patients who were unable to speak or move. Dr. Langston discovered that these people had all used a tainted form of heroin. Using fetal tissue transplant, two of the addicts recovered, garnering worldwide press coverage. This is the story behind the headlines" (from Alibris.com). Fascinating story.

Lieberman, Abraham, The Muhammad Ali Parkinson Center, *100 Questions & Answers About Parkinson Disease,* 2nd ed., Jones and Bartlett Publishers, 2011.

Lieberman is the author of several books about Parkinson's disease and has long been a prominent figure in national advocacy efforts and education in the field of Parkinson's research and patient care.

Mikkelsen, Anne Cutter, with Carolyn Stinson, *Take Charge of Parkinson's Disease: Dynamic Lifestyle Changes to Put You in the Driver's Seat,* DiaMedica Publishing, 2011.

Tons of information, ranging from Parkinson's-friendly recipes to personal stories about the author and her husband Mike, who has been living with Parkinson's for a long time and for whom she is a caregiver. Mikkelsen includes lifestyle and diet suggestions that are worthy of attention. She is an exquisitely talented haute cuisine chef who still loves to cook classic French fare, but with a healthier ingredients list.

Mischley, Laurie K., *Natural Therapies for Parkinson's Disease,* Coffeetown Press, 2010.

Dr. Mischley, who lives and practices in Seattle, is a pioneer in integrating naturopathic and complementary medicine with mainstream neuroscience to help neurological patients achieve better results from their treatment. This is an excellent and clearly presented body of information and a good resource for information on diet and use of supplements in an integrated strategy PWPs may find useful.

Okun, Michael S. and Hubert H. Fernandez, *Ask the Doctor about Parkinson's Disease,* Demos Health, New York, 2010.

Even a quick look reveals that this book's content is current and well-organized. The information is presented in question-and-answer format, with a separate section covering focused topics. Upon closer reading, the value of this book is revealed in generous helpings of information that is extremely relevant and useful for PWPs, especially someone like myself who is well into the course of the disease and hanging on for dear life to anything resembling a life with some degree of quality. Any PWP and/or her or his care partner will find much of interest in these pages. Readers will be that much better informed to ask their own neurologists relevant questions and become involved in their treatment plans.

Parkinson, James, *An Essay on the Shaking Palsy,* Classic Reprint Series, Forgotten Books, 2011 (originally published in 1817).

This is a reprint of the original essay by Dr. James Parkinson, after whom Parkinson's disease came to be known. Amazingly, Parkinson's essay, describing the syndrome he termed the shaking palsy, was written fewer than 50 years after the American Revolution (note that Parkinson was British), while the cause of the disease, not to mention a cure, remains an unsolved mystery today, almost two centuries later.

Theodoros, Deborah and Lorraine Ramig, *Communication and Swallowing in Parkinson's Disease,* Plural Publishing, Inc., 2011.

At first glance, this edited collection of related chapters seems to target the clinician rather than the general reader or Parkinson's patient, but in fact it begins with a cogent summary of parkinsonism accessible to just about anyone, then goes on to explore current relevant topics such as cognitive-linguistic disorders in Parkinson's disease and neuropathological bases for communication disorders in PD. This book is about Communication with a capital C—encompassing a broad range of behaviors and cognitive attributes of PWPs, not just the mechanics of speech and swallowing (not to minimize these problems). In addition, the list of cited works at the end of each chapter leaves no doubt that not a stone has been left unturned in the authors' efforts to gain a perspective and relevance level attainable only by good old sleeves-rolled-up scholarship.

Weiner, William J., Lisa M. Shulman, and Anthony E. Lang, *Parkinson's Disease: A Complete Guide for Patients and Families,* 2nd ed., Johns Hopkins Press, 2007.

Another good, generally useful resource book for PWPs and their care partners, this book received a 4.5-star customer rating on amazon.com. I've had a copy since it was first published and find that it is good in presenting some of the basic need-to-knows for recently diagnosed patients.

Postscript: Gathering Material

Yesterday was a bad day for me. Today, feeling like I'm on a steadier course, I sit down to write about what happened. It feels like a somewhat tedious endeavor, with a lot of disembodied ideas floating around in my head. Yesterday it was all so visceral, but now the ideas in my head are apparently disinclined to start adding up to anything of value or substance.

Music from the radio plays in the background. I stop trying so hard to reclaim the angst from the previous day and listen instead to Arlo Guthrie's beautiful song "In Times Like These," a lament about maintaining vision and faith through dark times. I could hear in Arlo's voice that conviction and depth that is impossible to manufacture or imitate. The message, more of a feeling, that I got from the song is that everything is important right now. This day, this moment, is not only the most important moment of my life, it is actually the only moment available to me in which I can act, love, grieve, regret, forgive, ignore, or make a choice—whether to stay alive or simply keep breathing. The drama of 24 hours ago seems suddenly less tempestuous, a weak storm which blew itself out overnight.

In the earlier afternoon yesterday I met with a married couple who are three years into the husband's PD diagnosis. We talked and drank beer for an hour or so, sitting out on the patio surrounded by lush May greenery, peony blossoms about to pop open, a climbing hydrangea sprouting life and legs, impatiens still not consumed by the does nursing their spring fawns.

I'd never met these people before but enjoyed making the connection and sharing stories and ideas about our respective lives with Parkinson's disease. But when they left, I felt empty, like I had nothing more to offer anyone. The question of identity resurfaced ("Who am I?"), underlining the need for a course correction that I spoke of earlier, in Chapter 2. I need to work with and be the person I am—and not mistake the collection of roles and abilities I have relied on for self-definition most of my life for whatever it is I mean or signify as a person.

During the past year or two, I like to think that I have been trying to find a true and open channel through a maze of dead ends and false leads in a richly fertile yet confoundingly intricate river delta system, seeking the one route that will take me past the river delta and out to the open sea. I've only begun to suspect what waits out there, in the deep blue waters where honesty and truth are found: Nothing. That's right, nothing, as in no thing. Both emptiness and salvation. Truth and honesty, revealed to one another without armor, caveats, hidden agendas, or expectations, begin to resemble love, which, according to a short-lived rock band I admire, is all we need.

Of course, shoal waters threaten to dump me into the river. Yesterday evening, in a crowded theater, I started crying during a profoundly moving performance about what it is like to have Parkinson's disease. The actor does in fact have PD. His recorded monologue and self-choreographed movement hit me like a ton of bricks; it blindsided me. As I started to identify with the emotional content of the moment, it was almost as if a cinematographer was shooting film just behind and over my right shoulder. The camera tracked with me, as though I was looking through a lens, as I left the theater, walked through the lobby, aware of being watched, and went outside where I sobbed against a a roughly hewn wooden post.

For what? For whom? I don't have the answer. But there was a thought growing in me that if this is life, then I am gathering material to write about it.

I remember Ram Dass saying (I paraphrase) that everybody wants to be where the action is, and the action is in emotion and interpersonal relationships. That's where things get interesting.

A recent movie, *Being Flynn,* stars Robert De Niro as Jonathan Flynn, a delusional writer on a downward spiral who encounters his grown son Nick at a homeless shelter (Nick is handing out bedding to clients, one of whom is his father).

"What are you doing here?" Nick asks the man who had essentially abandoned the boy and his mother years ago.

"I'm doing the same thing here as you're doing," Jonathan replies to Nick. "I'm gathering material."

"I'm not gathering material. This is my life," Nick says quietly.

"Life is gathering material," his father replies with a zealot's conviction. "What I am is an artist" De Niro continues. "Of course, writers, especially poets, are particularly prone to madness."

Gathering material. Artists. Madness. I sense a connection.

The actor William Hurt once said in an interview, "First comes the emotional breakdown. Then I can do the work." Yesterday, for me, constituted the breakdown, which became today's work, trying to interpret the material.

But it would be the height of cynicism to suggest that all the terrible, unfair, and ugly experiences that come our way over the course of a lifetime are really good because suffering makes great material for one's particular form of creative expression.

I write. More precisely, I write this book. I don't think of myself as a writer when I'm not writing anything, nor do I think of myself as a dancer when I am not dancing. Maybe, unwittingly, I am gathering material during those intermittent fallow periods. The "material" is not so much connected to who we are but to how we are. One role of art is to transform the material into a reflection of our inner lives as we experience love and passion as well as aging, illness, and dissolution. When the art is really good, the truth and the reflection are one and the same.

Not literally, but in some sense, the actor with Parkinson's disease whose portrayal of living with PD was so devastatingly insightful and concise, is me. I am both living that life and trying to turn it into some form of creative expression. I know every line of the play by heart, and I know that every line the actor delivers is true. I know, because that's my home. That's where I live.

photo by Jaynie Hancock

Made in the USA
Charleston, SC
22 January 2013